D1274006

CULTURE, PSYCHIATRY AND HUMAN VALUES

Publication No. 287

AMERICAN LECTURE SERIES®

A Monograph in

The BANNERSTONE DIVISION *of*

AMERICAN LECTURES IN PHILOSOPHY

Edited by

MARVIN FARBER, Ph.D.

Department of Philosophy
University of Buffalo
Buffalo, New York

CULTURE
PSYCHIATRY
and
HUMAN VALUES

The Methods and Values of a Social Psychiatry

By
MARVIN K. OPLER, Ph.D.
Department of Psychiatry
Cornell University Medical College
and New York Hospital (Payne Whitney Psychiatric Clinic)
New York, New York

With a Foreword by
THOMAS A. C. RENNIE, M.D.
Department of Psychiatry
Cornell University Medical College
and New York Hospital (Payne Whitney Psychiatric Clinic)
New York, New York

CHARLES C THOMAS · PUBLISHER
Springfield · Illinois · U.S.A.

301.732
O61e

CHARLES C THOMAS - PUBLISHER

BANNERSTONE HOUSE
301-327 East Lawrence Avenue, Springfield, Illinois, U.S.A.

Published simultaneously in the British Commonwealth of Nations by
BLACKWELL SCIENTIFIC PUBLICATIONS, LTD., OXFORD ENGLAND

Published simultaneously in Canada by
THE RYERSON PRESS, TORONTO

This monograph is protected by copyright. No part of it may be reproduced in any manner without written permission from the publisher.

Copyright 1956, by CHARLES C THOMAS - PUBLISHER

Library of Congress Catalog Card Number: 55-11703

RC
455
.06

Printed in the United States of America

To Thomas A. C. Rennie, M.D.,
scholar and friend

SEP 1 7 1962

FOREWORD

In the last few years we have witnessed the development of a branch of psychiatric activity and research worthy of the name of Social Psychiatry. Increasingly, as psychiatrists have met with anthropologists, sociologists, and other social scientists, a blending of knowledge from all the fields has taken place, and with this came the emergence of a common language, a point of view about personality and culture, and lately the sharp delineation of research projects which draw upon all these disciplines for their resolution.

The emergence of anthropology into the field of contemporary human behavior has brought substantial enlightenment to the problems of mankind in our own contemporary western civilization. Those of us who try to view man in his total cultural setting know that the contemporary anthropologist has much to contribute to our understanding of the inter-action of the person, his family, and his total cultural heritage.

Psychiatry and the social sciences have been in need of a critical review of what is known in this complex area. There is much that we can learn and insights that we can derive about our operating psychiatric hypotheses from the studies of cultures different from ours, as well as from a more systematic delineation of our own American cultural groups and what our specific culture does to man.

Dr. Opler is particularly fitted to prepare such a critical review for us and to synthesize the available knowledge. With years of anthropological experience behind him, he has acquired a wide knowledge of the pertinent and available studies and literature. For many years his own interest in personality functioning prepared him for his role as senior anthropologist in an interdisciplinary study of urban mental health in which he has been associated with me for three years as one of the principal investigators. This living experience in interdisciplinary thought and work has led to crystallization in this present volume.

In this volume Dr. Opler ranges widely through the whole field of cultural anthropology and psychodynamics, bringing to bear upon the reported studies a fresh and critical point of view, adhering to no particular school. He has also had the courage to scrutinize and challenge some long standing convictions and hypotheses. His own synthesis of the material is original and provocative.

Dr. Opler has given us a scholarly resume of mental illness as seen in the broad framework of cultural differences and determinants. I feel confident that this book will prove stimulating to scientists of many professional backgrounds. For psychiatrists particularly it illuminates new facets of personality development, of psychodynamics, and of some of the subtle cultural determinants of psychopathology.

I have learned much from Dr. Opler in my three years of work with him. This volume summarizes for me as a psychiatrist the salient anthropological concepts and views on mental illness which would otherwise have escaped me. I hope that it will do so for a large reading public.

THOMAS A. C. RENNIE, M.D.

Professor of Psychiatry (Social Psychiatry)
Cornell University Medical College

ACKNOWLEDGMENTS

I take pleasure in expressing my thanks and in making acknowledgments to the following editors and publishers for permission to quote from journal articles or books as the case may be; to the authors we are distinctly grateful:

To Dr. Clarence B. Farrar (editor) and *The American Journal of Psychiatry:* Volume 111, 1954, *The Psychopathologic Basis of Psychotherapy of Schizophrenia*, by Oskar Diethelm; Volume 110, 1953, *The Implications of the Psychogenetic Hypothesis*, by Paul Lemkau, Benjamin Pasamanik, and Marcia Cooper; Volume 109, 1952, *Some Characteristics of the Psychopathology of Schizophrenic Behavior in Bahian Society*, by Edward Stainbrook.

To Dr. Sol Tax (editor) and *The American Anthropologist:* Volume 44, 1942, *Some Psychological Aspects of Measurement Among the Salteaux*, by A. Irving Hallowell.

To Dr. Emil A. Gutheil (editor) and *The American Journal of Psychotherapy:* Volume 6, 1952, *The Concept of Normality*, by F. C. Redlich.

To *The Bulletin of the Menninger Clinic* and the following authors: Volume 18, 1954, *The Contribution of Psychoanalysis to American Psychiatry*, by Karl Menninger, and *The Perception Project: Progress Report*, by George S. Klein, P. Holtzman, and D. Laskin.

To Dr. C. West Churchman (editor) and *Philosophy of Science:* Volume 20, 1954, *The Concept of Values in Contemporary Philosophical Value Theory*, by Abraham Edel.

To Dr. J. O. Brew and the *Peabody Museum of Harvard University Papers:* Volume 47, 1952, *Culture: A Critical*

Review of Concepts and Definitions, by A. L. Kroeber and Clyde Kluckhohn.

To Harper and Brothers, *Social Psychology at the Cross-roads* (edited by John H. Rohrer and Muzafer Sherif): Cultural Factors in the Structuralization of Perception, by A. Irving Hallowell, Copyright, 1951.

To Harvard University Press: *Chamorros and Carolinians of Saipan*, by Alice Joseph and V. F. Murray, Copyright, 1951.

To The University of Chicago Press: *Principles of Intensive Psychotherapy*, by Frieda Fromm-Reichman, Copyright, 1951; and *Mental Disorders in Urban Areas*, by R. E. L. Faris and H. W. Dunham, Copyright, 1939.

To Henry Holt and Company: *Human Nature and Conduct*, by John Dewey, Copyright, 1922.

To Blackwell Scientific Publications, Limited, *Prospects in Psychiatric Research* (edited by J. M. Tanner): Points of Research into the Interaction Between the Individual and the Culture, by Aubrey Lewis, Copyright, 1953.

To The Milbank Memorial Fund Quarterly, *Mental Hygiene and Socio-Environmental Factors:* Volume 26, 1948, by Robert H. Felix and R. V. Bowers.

To The New American Library of World Literature, *About the Kinsey Report*, (edited by D. P. Geddes and Enid Curie): Sex and Character, by Erich Fromm, Copyright, 1948.

To Grune and Stratton, *Current Problems in Psychiatric Diagnosis*, (edited by P. Hoch and J. Zubin): Prognosis in the Psychoneuroses—Benign and Malignant Developments, by T.A.C. Rennie, Copyright, 1953.

To Appleton-Century-Crofts, *The Unconscious: A Symposium*, (edited by E. S. Drummer): The Unconscious Patterning of Behavior in Society, by Edward Sapir, Copyright, 1948.

To Yale University Press: *An Essay on Man*, by E. Cassirer, Copyright, 1944.

To W. W. Norton and Company: *Psychosocial Medicine*, by J. L. Halliday, Copyright, 1948.

I also wish to express my gratitude to Dr. Oskar Diethelm and Dr. T. A. C. Rennie who read the manuscript and offered helpful suggestions, and to Mrs. Doris Slawson who typed the final draft. Any errors, however, are of my own commission.

Last, but not least, to Charlotte Opler and to Ruth and Lewis, our children, go my appreciation for their warm, and by now perennial indulgence of what are known as scholarly pursuits.

M. K. O.

CONTENTS

xiii

CULTURE, PSYCHIATRY AND HUMAN VALUES

PART I

SOCIAL AND CULTURAL BACKGROUNDS
OF MENTAL ILLNESS

INTRODUCTION

THE IMPACT of social and cultural environment upon the development of personalities is the central concern of social psychiatry. While this environment is in no sense a fixed form of pattern into which personality falls and is moulded, neither is it simply a mere extraneous influence added to inevitable results determined by the child-rearing practices of a culture. The attempts to exaggerate the socio-cultural setting to a global and inclusive mould effect are daily belied by the variations in personalities encountered by observers, scientific or otherwise, in any given setting. On the other hand, even the most cursory acquaintance with psychiatric case histories individually considered indicates the crudity of beginning with the Freudian basic disciplines and inferring therefrom the total contours of adult personality configurations. Both methods, the grossly cultural and the rigidly psychogenetic, are only partly useful as formulae and only partly true to individual and cultural realities.

These theoretical opposites fail in that they do not assess, beyond the one-way causal scheme either for psychiatry or anthropology, the exact relationship that environmental experiences bear *throughout* the life history to individual adjustment. As Edward Sapir once said, "The worlds in which different societies live are distinct worlds, not merely the same world with different labels attached." In connection with Princeton's Perception Demonstration Center, Hadley Cantril has shown how the nature of the indi-

5

vidual's experience in life, even upon the perceptual level, depends on his prior assumptions, how these in turn are built from past experiences; and how attitudes, opinions and percepts change only when the individual is blocked and feels frustration. No doubt, turning to psychiatry, a building up of cognitive, attitudinal and perceptual patterns has also an organic, metabolic and hormonal basis since the organism, as such, is the reactive mechanism; however, personality is more than mechanism, and the individual is more than an autonomic system, self-propelled and self-motivated.

Ordinarily, a person's experiences are in the normal course interpreted along lines laid down by his culture, even though the channels cut by culture thread through such more familiar terrain as family structure and functioning, a system of values and beliefs, a range of social and economic statuses, certain practices and taboos, attitudes towards health and illness, and such features as the characteristic styles of interpersonal relationships. All of these features are the coin of the realm of personality formation, affecting marital, parent-child, sibling, peer, and other group relations. They vary with culture, and with degree and pace of acculturation or culture change. Among the basic orientations provided by culture, A. I. Hallowell has recently listed self- and object-orientation, spatio-temporal orientation, a motivational orientation, and a sense of normative standards and values.[1] The kinds of relationships set up within a culture and defining its age-groups, its sex behavior and attitudes, its statements of the individual position in the family and in the social group are no doubt ramifications of these basic categories. They may be seen also in what Ruth Benedict once called the continuities and discontinuities of the life history pattern.

This life span, or life cycle, is lived in a constant homeostatic relationship with this total environment, parts of which become internalized and implicit in an individual's responses and reactions as well as external and explicit. On the individual level of responses in actions and symbols, unique though these are, no life is lived alone and apart from interpersonal patterns of communication and inter-action. All personality formation, or the psychodynamics of well or ill alike, rely in the last analysis upon symbolic forms of communication and self-expression in which what is human *and* cultural is shared, while that which is bizarre and autistic is closer to raw impulse or guarded illusion. A psychiatry, or a behavioral science, which credits a human being with a dynamic life biography and with con-ditions of existence in communicated and felt socio-cul-tural settings, but which ends by denying reality of the social and cultural groups, cannot move from case A to case B, or indeed fully assess the impact of other people on either A or B.[2]

In his recent posthumous work, *The Interpersonal Theory of Psychiatry*, Harry Stack Sullivan has stated that progress toward a "psychiatry of peoples" can emerge only from improved understanding of significant patterns of living in the modern world coupled with the discovery of import-ant details in personality development by which persons of different socio-cultural background "come to manifest more or less adequate behavior in their given social set-tings." Each of these lines of inquiry, the first in anthro-pology and the second in social psychiatry, he regarded as a "necessary supplement to the other." Seen from this vantage point, not merely the often unrecallable earlier stages of childhood confusion, but any appropriate and less dereistic or painful points in the life cycle are equally im-portant in their own right "in the unfolding of possibilities for interpersonal relations in the progression . . . toward mature competence for life in a fully human world." The importance of families, communities, socio-political entities, group cultures and sub-cultures as the settings for these progressive efforts of the individual are all alluded to by Sullivan. He also stresses the special skills in the study of interpersonal relationships, participant observation and interviewing techniques using the operational approach and field theory concepts of psychiatric and anthropological science. Finally, we learn that, ideally, the psychiatrist as "participant observer" uses concepts derived from the anthropologist's analyses of other cultures.[3]

This concordance of interests in the fields of psychiatry and anthropology in three areas, the individual personality, the cultural background, and family or social group participation is a convergence in broadly integrative behavioral science. That it should appear in the consolidating and synthesizing phases of each discipline in the Twentieth Century is not surprising. If, as has been known for some time, there are intimate connections between the organization of personality and its socio-cultural background, then the study of either is revealing of outlines, demarcations and significances of conduct in the individual.

The increasing use of projective test methodologies in the study of cultures is instructive at this juncture, since it was Rorschach himself who first studied psychotic patients from two different Swiss cantons and who reported that the results obtained seemed to indicate variation in the actual form of psychoses which could be attributed to distinct cultural backgrounds. The ease with which the Rorschach, and other projective techniques, could be administered even to nonliterate peoples, and the objective criterion of "blind analyses" by psychologists who did not know the informant, opened the way for on-the-spot ethnologists to gather reasonably unbiased personality data. It is no wonder that psychologists, interpreting such materials with scoring systems which were not even well-established in our culture, found these to fall short of adequate quantitative establishment of norms elsewhere and were consequently guided by intelligent use of the raw materials and by general principles governing the use of the total instrument.

The underlying Rorschach principles, or assumptions, that the individual had no way of knowing what was expected in terms of performance and therefore characteristically responded in the way in which he handled every life situation seemed true enough if one further assumed inherent grouping principles in the perception of form, as promulgated by Gestalt psychology, and secondly, recognized the possibility of cross-cultural differences and comparisons. Indeed, Hallowell showed that certain responses were popularly given despite strongly divergent cultural backgrounds.[4] On the other hand, Laura Thompson, in a study of three different Hopi communities with variance in economic security and social organization, demonstrated through projective material the importance of cultural background and varying social organization in the personalities of members of each group.[5] Hallowell, even earlier, found significant Rorschach differences among acculturated and unacculturated Salteaux.[6]

The techniques of separate or blind analyses, initiated by the anthropologist, Cora DuBois, and Oberholzer in DuBois' *The People of Alor*, were continued with inclusion of the Thematic Apperception Test by the anthropologist Thomas Gladwin and the clinical psychologist, Seymour B. Sarason, in their joint work, *Truk; Man in Paradise.*[7] In such blind interpretations, there is remarkable similarity in interpretations given by ethnologists and clinicians, as where, in the last example, Sarason was able to draw conclusions, similar to Gladwin, about the concentration of Trukese on rigid suppression of feelings and impulses, and on the development of conformance and concreteness of thinking in these subjects. Actually, the anthropological data on the all-important lineage relationships proved to be of crucial significance in explaining the development of conforming, inhibited, suppressing personalities. On the other hand, the psychological data revealed a dominance of women and forced an ethnological re-examination of the material wherein, though seemingly more submissive, they did indeed occupy the truly pivotal position in social organization because of their primary role in the handling of food allocations. With these basic orientations in mind, purely descriptive data including male and female sexual conduct, family organization and even child-rearing practices fall in line. Equally, records examined by Oberholzer, and revealing kinds of reaction typical of patients suffering brain injury in our culture, were adequately understandable only when cultural themes and organization were explicit. In the Trukese study, an important sexual problem of women was missed in Rorschach interpretations of the psychologist by merely not knowing the female sexual symbol.

Jules Henry has pointed out that the use of rare detail in Rorschachs of a jungle people of South America is a function of their need to observe their surroundings in order to survive. Similarly, Cook's finding of "overuse" of space-responses in Samoa reflected simply the special cultural value attached to the color white. The point is clear that in two sciences related to social psychiatry, in cultural anthropology and clinical psychology, there is increasing awareness that in order to understand both culture and personality adequately, one must ascertain how the personality of the members of a given society finds expression *within a social and cultural framework*. Three-dimensional social psychiatry, involving the techniques of social science and psychology, would likewise require as a necessary parameter of scientific observation the notion of a socio-cultural frame of reference for normative and aberrant; for gauging the intensities of affect; the types and degrees of human expressivity in different cultures; the choice of cultural symbols used in human communication; or in short, the varying cognitive, perceptual and attitudinal interpretations of any cultural human being.

Awareness of these generalized, or cultural, symbolic functions in individual psychodynamics is not limited to psychology. The fact that human communication and expression is based on symbols to which meanings are assigned was discovered, so to speak, independently in psychiatry once the notion of an inevitable course of illness and rigid diagnostic categories, as in the classical descriptive work of Kraepelin, gave way to a more dynamic view of variables in typology, illness progression, and environmental influences as in the work of Adolf Meyer. With the gradual death of the notion of a "unit psychosis," the ideological importance of longitudinal case history grew, relying at first on relating the organic and metabolic functioning to unique symbolic functioning of personality. Gradually, the hospital as a therapeutic milieu, "push therapy," the phenomena of transference and countertransference, and explorations into symbolic content and dynamics came into purview. The movement was from hospitalized to ambulatory treatment where possible; from custodial care and descriptive analysis to devices aimed at gradual socialization and improved environment; from cross-sectional symptomatology to assessment of the longitudinal course of illness; and from random exploration and probing to carefully guided support and re-education.

Increasingly the psychosocial position required a knowledge of the cultural setting and background of each patient to the end that his world of meanings and experiences be assessed in therapy, and his organic and symbolic functioning understood in terms of the contexts or milieus of family, community, social and sub-cultural groups in which he had played a role. Independently, in the social sciences, the areas of social action and interactive process were explored in social systems and social roles. The social statuses and their functions in the social structure, and the manner in which that structure was systematized were all important ingredients in defining an individual's relationships to his fellows, and his activities, to be sure, in relation to theirs. Nevertheless, the anatomy and physiology of a social system and its functioning related ultimately to a further system of meanings, at once cultural and personal in essence. This was to say that roles were, by and large, culturally defined; that social structures varied with cultural backgrounds and identities, and that whole social systems were built on foundations supplied by what Kluckhohn called implicit (Sapir's "unconsciously patterned") and explicit (consciously followed) cultural symbols.

In the work of Adolf Meyer, the challenge to an oversimplified and rigid typology and labeling process was to construct new typologies having greater range and also greater reference to the variability of process in the adaptation, or maladaptation, to environment. In therapy, too, one of his contributions was to point to possibilities of adaptation to a milieu, or to point up positive relationships which a patient was in a position to utilize. In the same intellectual period, John Dewey in philosophy was noting that a social existence was a necessary condition for the development of normative mentation processes in any individual. Physical anthropologists like Boas were pointing out the mutational plasticity of humans under environmental changes; social biologists like Hogben were documenting environmental effects in the statistical incidence of mental deficiency; and H. S. Jennings was initiating the studies of human behavior and genetics which have led ultimately to our present knowledge that of the more than five hundred single gene substitutions for which there is good evidence, only a minor few determine behavioral resultants. The psychoanalytic movement, least "organicist" of all, was at the same time enjoying a growth of popularity in the United States while giving rise to sharply varying systems like those of Horney, of Roheim, of Rado, Kardiner and Ferenczi, which like Sullivan's were directly influenced by anthropologists such as Sapir and Linton, Kluckhohn, Benedict and Mead.

In none of this transfer of interest to total life span, to situational context or milieu, to relationships within a social system, and to cultural background, were the sacred precincts of any one science inviolable. Multidisciplinary research recognized that the pathology of a society reflects its general conditions, and conversely offered important clues to an understanding of the culture. Galen's ancient phase, "Man is a whole with his environment," found epidemiological confirmation not in the least from carefully designed public health inquiries in which the epidemiology (*how much* illness in time periods of incidence) soon came to mean *how much* illness emerged in relation to age, sex, and finally social and cultural strata. Why these problems of incidence and prevalence mean very little for certain kinds of illness such as mental disorder, unless at the same time etiological problems of the same illness groups are attacked, is a matter which will be discussed below. Suffice it to say the scenes were set for interest in the *how and why* of mental illness by a study of the incidence or occurrences of different psychopathological states in persons of specific socio-cultural background.

Psychiatry, par excellence, is a science which specializes in a knowledge of the way human experience is utilized in the total economy of personality; psychiatrists soon realized that as a generalizing behavioral science it must press beyond individual case formulations to psychosocial typologies. Indeed, J. L. Halliday in his *Psychosocial Medicine*[8] defines illness in general as "a reaction, or mode of behavior, or vital expression of a living unit in response to those forces which he encounters as he moves and grows in time." Etiology of mental illness is studied in terms of dual, relational causes which lie both in the nature of the individual and in the nature of his environment, *but in both at the same time*. While a culture is, at any point in time, more massive and imposing than any individual participant and must be distinguished from the individual, the great danger in multidisciplinary research involving relational causal systems, is to so abstract the individual from his meaningful cultural background that he ceases to be a responsive or live subject for diagnosis, case formulation or psychotherapy. There are are simply no individuals apart from specific socio-cultural background.

By culture we then mean an imposing and conditioning variable which always becomes internalized, in one way or another, in the psychic systems of human beings. Far from being a mere matter of the artifacts and social organization of a people, culture also contains their range of expressive symbolism, whether in art, language, dance or song, or in the non-verbal communication patterns involved in gestures, interpersonal emotional contacts, and the rules governing relationships of age groups and of sexes. It:[9]

"consists of patterns, explicit and implicit, of and for behavior acquired and transmitted by symbols, constituting the distinctive achievement of human groups, including their embodiments in artifacts; the essential core of culture consists of traditional (i.e., historically derived and selected) ideas and especially their attached values; culture systems may, on the one hand, be considered as products of action, on the other as conditioning elements of further action."

More specifically, it includes the patterned family and social influences, the means of symbolic communication forged into a way of life, affirmed and reaffirmed in the common currency of custom, and most importantly, always having a significant discernible meaning and value for the individual.

That these traditional ideas, or themes of culture influencing patterns of behavior; the prevailing ethics, the child-rearing practices, the notions of social integration, the taboos, religious values, and attitudes toward health and illness; that these leitmotifs of a culture were precipitates of history or could influence history was probably not the main fact about them. Surely the dynamic interplay of factors within culture influenced history. But equally important, at least for behavioral science, was the manner in which these elements in a way of life became incorporated in individual functioning, how much or to what extent ego involvements became dependent on them, and why they had much to do, positively or negatively, with super-ego functioning.

The tendency, in the Freudian view, to equate culture and super-ego, as in *Totem and Taboo*, was a needless oversimplification. Not all in culture, except in Dr. Pangloss' "best of all possible worlds" is positive, sublimated, humanly helpful and real achievement. Even more serious, human impulses, perceptions, emotionalized attitudes and knowledge are dependent upon cultural circumstances. The tendency to regard "normal" or "social" behavior as the sublimated, cultural achievement, and "culture" as due to successful repression or identity of feelings with others (both formulated in *Totem and Taboo*) begs two questions. May there not be what Jahoda has called "indiscriminate adjustment through passive acceptance of environmental conditions" as distinct from inability to adjust, or different from active mastery and adjustment? Secondly, the negative, destructive experiences likewise felt by the organism and interpreted on perceptual, cognitive and attitudinal levels (Rado's destructive emotions as opposed to welfare emotions) are, no matter how far from personal self-fulfillment, still caught in the same web of cultural circumstances.

If psychosomatic responding to stress or psychic distorting reactions to frustration are found, they are nevertheless referable to felt experience within a cultural framework. It has been suggested that emotion *is* bodily change plus attitudes stemming from experience, in the cumulative work of men like W. B. Cannon, Harold Wolff, or William Grace.[10] Animal experimentation on emotional conditioning has also, even in a non-cultural setting, led to similar conclusions.[11] It remains to relate emotionally charged attitudes in humans to the cultural settings and contexts, stressful or beneficial, in which they eventuate.

Therefore, while cultures are not to be confused with unique clinical cases, or with negative clinical formulations, they do contain *stress systems* of a generalized character which are capable of differentiation, one from another, and which have considerable clinical importance. Attempts to define these in terms of social structure alone, or by rates of interaction of persons in a social structure, may be misleading. Indeed, in anthropology, whole schools or systems have been developed and abandoned, on the premise that types of social structure and interactional systems may be studied alone and apart from the psychological qualifications of the *meanings of cultural conduct for individuals*. Such a system was Radcliffe-Brown's at Chicago in the 1930's, or the Chapple and Coon equilibrium-disequalibrium theories of social interaction at Harvard in the 1940's.

But if culture, social system and personality are functional variables, they are interdependent and interrelated. As concerns the always unique and personalized systems of affect and thought in any individual, it is always the *individual* who hopes, thinks, acts, dreams and aspires. Nevertheless, each individual has a particular place in social structure of a definable sort and a particular set of cultural beliefs and conditionings in his background. There is no longer serious doubt as to the overwhelming importance of life history in mental illness, but the relevance of social and cultural background in furnishing guide lines to this personalized life cycle remains to be explored.

Beginning with Kraepelin, it has been known that psychopathological illness varies in content and in type with culture. Ziehen noted variations in Holland and in German Thuringia. Bleuler, in Switzerland, remarked upon differences in English and Irish cases, Bavarians and Saxons; speaking of his own hospital, he wrote: "Indeed, in our hospital, it is easy to note the difference between the reactions of the Bernese as compared with the Zurichois who are quite closely related racially."[12] P. M. Yap has described the Latah reaction in Malaya, Arctic Hysteria in Siberia, and Imu in Hokkaido.[13] In the same British journal of psychiatry, E. H. Hare reports on variations in the Congo, Papua and India; while J. Carothers in 1947 compared incidence data among Africans of Kenya with those of American Negroes.[14] An analysis of the possible significance of these patterns of cross-cultural variances will be given below. To date, they have largely followed a rather euphoric pattern: Faris in 1934 finding no schizophrenias in Belgian Congo; Seligman in 1929 finding no protracted mental disorders in Papua, merely brief attacks; unless acculturated to the west, Seligman and Dhunjibhoy's data (1930) locating no schizophrenias, unless like Parsees, the people were highly advanced in "Western civilization"; Carothers' Kenya colonists having low incidence or disorder and with freedom from most of our social, sexual and economic problems "in consequence" having no "obsessional neuroses"; the Okinawans, unexposed to concepts of sin and guilt, being reported as notably free of anxiety and all neuroses.

For the United States, the best known statistics are of a different order. Of all persons hospitalized, psychiatric disorder equals the number of cases for all other illnesses combined; of these mental illnesses, more than half are nonorganic schizophrenias, depressive states or severe psychoneuroses. Beyond this are those ambulatory, in private care or receiving no treatment whatsoverer. The probably conservative estimate of one out of twelve infants suffering from mental disease in his later life course, or one out of sixteen Americans ill now, does not include the psychological components in psychosomatic ailments (asthma, allergies, migraine, rhinitis, urticaria, neurodermatitis, ulcerative colitis, peptic ulcer, nonglandular obesity, essential hypertension, etc.), nor does it include the 20,000 suicides per year, the accident-prone, that part of crime and delinquency described by Wertham and Redl, marital discord and divorce, and such problems as impotence and frigidity. Further, there are countless cases of minor compulsions, private phobias, and transient hysteriform simulations of certain diseases. A sardonic wit has called this The Aspirin Age of the Atomic Era in Urban America.

Before the ethical or philosophic questions that this problem raises, there are first the scientific, methodological ones. The psychosocial position has supplanted what Felix and Bowers call "the older assumptions of geographic or biological determinism of human behavior . . . the product of climate, heredity or original sin."[15] In place of the solitary individual governed by such somewhat fateful and extraneous forces, Jahoda speaks of a human need for "active adjustment," "attempts at mastery of environment", "the ability to perceive correctly the world and himself," and mental health as a dynamic concept, not simply a state of being.

Human energies which utilize symbolic human constructs in interpersonal communication may do so for
better or worse, but they will not act solely on behalf of a
biological unit, or emotionalized *id* impulses except in the
most poorly integrated personalities.   What Freud interpreted as raw impulse, basic need and earliest cathected
orientations are better seen in the continuum of adaptive
adjustment in which impulse, need and cathexis are always
modified, early in life to be sure, in the area of interpersonal communication.   That integration of "mental" and
emotional functions, or even cognitive adequacy, or
personal insight, may be won or lost in discrete personal
histories should not blind us to the fact that real, interpersonal contacts in a common, workaday world always help
to define the limits of the normative and the aberrant.
Within this framework, the nonintegration or the thought
disturbance, or lack of judgment implied in any disorganizing illness is not there as non-conformity in the narrow sense
of majority tastes and aspirations.   It is the result of communicated and felt emotionality that is destructive, that is
a part of no normative group, however small, no positive
social force, and no tradition of a sustaining sort.   Even
bohemian literary and artistic movements have been
aimed accurately at lace-curtained salons of dead art.
There should be no confusion of regimentation with functional movements, or with principles of positive conformance.   Aberration is not innovation.

It is no longer believed in most quarters that the circumstances which lead the individual inexorably into some
tortured world "of his own making" are really of his making.   Nor is the determinism of today one which stresses
such isolated events as nursing or weaning, or the various
swaddling or swathing practices of Czech, Slovak, Italians,
Russians, or Polish to be read off as modal personality
determinants.   The individual as a psychosocial unit,

capable of tremendous emotional expression, is subject to adaptive adjustment in such a way that while his experience, to be sure, is always felt and motivated, ordinarily that pattern of experience has itself context and meaning, integration, and considerable reaffirmation before it may achieve any emotional hue. If psychological field theory and anthropological behavior studies have proved anything, they have taught that while it is always the individual who functions adequately, (or who may otherwise despair, hallucinate, hate, compensate, fear, or withdraw) he is nevertheless one, in either case, whose experiences are largely imposed from without, become immediately involved in an integration of sorts, are felt within and interpreted along lines laid down by a whole series of social and cultural events. Before styles of interpersonal relationship reach individual "minds and hearts," they are subject to the greater statistical weight and frequency of socio-cultural group phenomena.

As Benedict, Horney, and Redlich have noted, each in separate ways,[16] the cultural norms and standards are present to help define both normal and aberrant. While psychiatry has noted a certain patterning, or typology, in certain disease processes, it remains to investigate specific cultural scenes and the pathology within them, to locate the effectively charged points in the cultural stress systems. There is no reason to feel that a culture may not be studied and diagrammed for ambiguities, conflicts, discontinuities in life course, obvious stress features, and handicaps to maturation and healthy development. Reaction formations, premised from one case to the next on typical anxieties, fears, hates, confusions and lack of positive communication within such systems may be balanced against studies of "normals" from matched circumstances within a culture to learn what readings of the cultural map develop the well and ill. When this is done, the functions (and limits) of both destructive and welfare emotions will be fully understood within the systems of human communication in which they alone have meaning.

This connection of culture and social group, not with modal personality constructs of dubious value clinically, but with statistically oriented epidemiology and psychiatrically valid studies of the etiology of health and illness, is the course suggested for social psychiatry. At this point, no other course, it is felt, can link experience with expression in human symbolic communication systems, or deal adequately in the triadic systems of culture, social group and personality, with such related patterns as values and attitudes; the same linkage exists between world outlooks and personal horizons, the social position of the sexes and actual sexual behavior, the status system and characteristic styles of interpersonal behavior, or in brief, between culture and personality. Since these relationships are already well known in anthropological monographs across the earth's surface, the obvious need is application to psychiatric phenomena. Let us therefore plot the course, theoretically, which marks the normative, usual experience in relation to that which marks out the aberrant.

Since both courses are functionally important, or operationally used, by the individual, a dynamic and graphic analogy may be apposite. It is suggested as an alternative to the individually centered (and limited) theory of id, ego and super-ego.

The normal, usual experience is the road most people, representing the creative aspects of a culture at its best, can follow. They take it, not simply as individuals but in groups, each with a life span and with certain age, sex and organic attributes. The line of persons and of families following the course are only in unusual systems, rigid and restrictive, in a tight line. Instead there are all the alternative routings, the by-passes, the room for occasional choice and the variant speeds, stops, impediments and hazards. The vehicles to such accomplishment are culturally designed and constructed. Generally, they vary in age within automotive or historical limits, in aspects of design and purpose, the truck and town sedan even in functional class reference. Beyond the "cultural" make and construction, denoted by name, and the "class" or usage functions, denoted by structure, there are the differentiated motives of drivers. (In view of the penchant for making individual motivational systems "basic" to some systems of social psychology, we shall add that the make or construction, the cultural label on any car, together with age, implies much, realistically considered, as to what pure motivation can really accomplish in the driver's seat.)

The road hazards or conditions, and the make or type of car, we prefer to think of as the different conditions of culture. The former might be called, in this metaphor, the cultural stress system; the latter, the vehicle intended for human accomplishment of purposes and goals, we mean to be the cultural modalities, or means, for such achievement. But some drivers, some motivational systems as it were, doubtlessly because of the hazards and stresses, the inadequacies of the vehicle and its continuing strain on the adjustive motivational system, abandon the trip and set off—presumably afoot and with certainly less efficiency—on the pathways and trails with no certain markings, armed only with their primitive energies and impulses, and with only remnants of their original purpose. We submit that the topography, the strains, the barriers, impediments and roadblocks have something to do, even as to their place of location in the journey, with the points that mark out the bypaths, the impractical shortcuts, and the meandering lonely trails.

Note one fact about the lonely trails, the ten percent of mental disorder. Epidemiologically considered, they are not wholly unique pathways, as clinical experience on similar cases, or statistics on given nosological entities indicate. As history changes and cultures vary, new styles of mental illness arise and are described. The phrase, "worlds of their own making," has little meaning in view of the Dancing Mania, or Tarantism, of Thirteenth Century Italy, described by Ferdinandus and Baglivi and redescribed by Sigerist. The imagined tarantula bite felt in the dull slack of hot summer seasons sent people to streets and market places to dance together in gay, almost ceremonial attire, until insensate or carried away. The Mania, which spread in Europe for a few centuries reads strangely like the Vailala Madness of New Guinea, reported by F. E. Williams for the dislocated, acculturated areas of that island; it is reminiscent also of certain aspects of the Ghost Dance of the Plains, described by Cora DuBois, or the Ute Indian Ghost Dance (M. K. Opler). Studies like Cantril's of the invasion from Mars, or the Mattoon, Illinois hysteria; the Beloi cult of the BaThonga or the Vada sorcery of the Trobiands; or Latah and Imu reactions demonstrate that there is little about mental illness which is immutable in time or hard to duplicate cross-culturally in special times and places. Yet if we are not hopelessly to chronicle the cross-cultural phenomena in separate, unrelated studies, the study of well and ill within the settings of modern, populous cultures and sub-cultures, including our own, is next in order.

Psychopathological differences may be expected in modern cultures. As Parsons and Shils have recently pointed out, *all* cultures regulate social and sexual behavior, control organized activities, and affect traditional behavior of any sort through processes of symbolic communication.[17] This means, at the very least, that all areas of perception, feeling and evaluation are culturally differentiated during the period when a child first experiences meaningful contacts with adults by the learning of language or by the development of what Piaget might call a social sense. Wayne Dennis' studies of infancy differentiation among Navajo and Hopi children in the Thirties and Forties, or those of Rene Spitz and John Bowlby showing the importance of maternal figures in early maturation, lend support. A variety of anthropological data points to a continuing process of differentiation, through life span. The full-length biography and a variety of personal documents were proposed early by Sapir and Kluckhohn as a firm way of testing the impact of culture upon personality.

In social psychiatry, and in ethnopsychiatric surveys such as J. C. Carothers' *The African Mind*, the study of individual patients, or of symptomatology and psychodynamics of individual disorders, has broadened into concern for the ambulatory patient and, finally, to consideration of the person in his community and sociocultural setting. As yet, few studies have been made in the kind of modern scene, marked by ethnic and status contrasts, which assure us that modernized urban cultural heterogeneity has been studied at all. A total stock-taking of methodological problems involved in epidemiological study in the United States and Europe is required. Below, in brief outline, some of the chief problems of such epidemiology are presented. They are then developed in reference to given studies in subsequent sections.

I

METHODOLOGICAL CONSIDERATIONS IN SOCIAL PSYCHIATRY

RELATIONSHIP OF EPIDEMIOLOGY AND ETIOLOGY IN THE STUDY OF MENTAL ILLNESS

IN ADVANCING social psychiatry beyond its present range of knowledge, the striking results in epidemiology, now limited to scattered and exotic parts of the world, must be extended to contemporary Western cultures. When Western studies of epidemiology are reviewed critically, the lack of articulation and significant connection between clinical studies on the one hand and sociocultural studies on the other is notable. At the outset, one is forced to agree with a recent statement by Felix and Bowers that the search for environmental factors has not yielded, as yet, any full understanding of their importance.[18] In only a few studies have psychiatrists and social scientists collaborated at all, in fewer still has this collaboration been aimed at the contemporary urban scene, and in only a mere handful has this collaborative effort involved fully the special techniques of each discipline.

In his discussion of *The Psychopathologic Basis of Psychotherapy of Schizophrenia*, Diethelm notes, " . . . The cultural influences have been considered in recent years, but were insufficiently emphasized because one has not studied sufficiently the development of individual schizophrenic illnesses over a period of 30 to 40 years, nor the changing psychopathology with changes in our own culture." Continuing later with an account of the influences of the original Freudian group upon such men as Bleuler, Jung and Abraham of the Burghölzli Clinic, Diethelm states:

" . . . Outstanding symptoms were those which could be best interpreted by the concept of regression to oral and anal levels of personality development. It is of interest to note that in a hospital with modern dynamic therapy in which interpersonal influences are constantly analyzed and studied, these symptoms of regression of 40 years ago have become rare or have disappeared completely. To this group belong incontinence, smearing, eating of feces, so-called fetal postures, verbigeration, echolalia, refusal to eat, frank catatonic motility disorders, vulgarity in words and in symbolic acts, stereotypies and mannerisms. These changes do not seem to relate to suppression or repression, but rather to lack of activation of oral and anal factors by the changed environmental attitudes and behavior."

In his total account of the essential aspects of the psychotherapy of schizophrenia, Diethelm lays proper stress upon the need "to be constantly guided by dynamic psychopathology, with a recognition of physical, environmental and cultural influences".[19] Scarcely any study of an *epidemiological* sort has combined these criteria in research on any given mental illness though Barrabee, Zborowski, and Diethelm have conducted etiological studies within ethnic sub-groups having a qualitative if not quantitative aim. Barrabee's study of psychotics of certain backgrounds is aided by psychiatric information and cultural inquiry, Zborowski's on pain reactions only partly fulfills the psychiatric criteria on dynamic psychopathology, and Diethelm's and Barnett's on alcoholism, containing, for example, negative findings on urban Chinese, discovers interesting relationships of this reaction to personality structure and numerous cultural relationships while insisting, no doubt rightly, that alcoholism is not, in itself, a mental illness. These studies, however, point the way to the kind of etiological information which is needed in any epidemiological inquiry.

When one turns from Diethelm's formulation on variability in illness typology, variation in course of illness, and change in symptomatology in accordance with changing cultural scene back to the usual, or basic, presentations of psychoanalytic dynamics, one is struck by the need to review these dynamic formulae in the light of external influences and a more variable typology than is commonly used. In psychoanalytic dynamics, such typical mechanisms as regression, repression, projection and introjection, and their concomitants, displacement and substitution, rationalization and overcompensation, or identification and sublimation are applied to mankind *sub specie aeternitatis*. These mechanisms are discussed as if only the classical Viennese cases existed, with neither environmental nor cultural variations. Of course, much could be said for elaboration of the original Freudian insights under a variety of different influences, not the least of these being cultural and environmental change. However, a wholly mechanistic conception of these dynamics persists in some quarters, so much so that variable dynamics are lost in the rigidity of a single, orthodox point of view. Even worse, cultural subtleties and shadings are not, on occasion, recognized at all.

In opposition to the wholly erroneous idea that human behavior is subject to one typical course, dynamically speaking, and that mankind exists *sub specie aeternitatis*, it may be said that, culturally speaking, what is repressed varies, as does the availability of role models for identification. Further, who is or what becomes the target for projection, and what cultural channels for regression or sublimation are open to a person of a given sex, age and cultural background are all matters of considerable importance. It is not merely that the mechanisms of an individual's adjustment are culturally influenced, but that his *type* of adjustment *in the first place* may relate to cultural background factors. If, for example, there is no latency period, as is well known, in the Trobriands; if Zuni women feel little social sense of deprivation; Okinawans, no great sexual shame or guilt; or Samoans little spontaneity and personal freedom in contrast to Navajos; then not only do the mechanisms of adjustment vary, but the basic emotionality involved in a type of adjustment will vary as well.

While epidemiology in social psychiatry has meant the indications of an incidence and prevalence of psychiatric disorders in relation to variable social and cultural strata, the key term, mental illness, convinces one immediately that etiological factors bearing upon psychopathology are of primary importance. In a logical sense, etiology (how mental illness arises) determines epidemiology (the incidence of illness in given time periods). In the biosocial position as well, the impact of the sociocultural environment upon personality development, an etiological question, underlies epidemiological results. The first problem, therefore, in multidisciplinary research of this order is to indicate the socio-cultural environment *in its possible relation* to psychiatric disorder. Since no research worthy of note flies blind amid winds of doctrine and currents of interest, the formulation of hypothetical questions will be fast, accurate and relevant to basic problems only where the suppositions of contributing sciences are examined for pertinence and power of explanation relative to this kind of phenomena, psychiatric disorder. There is little point, in view of the scarcity of research in this field, to test the environment for dynamically irrelevant details. A. N. Whitehead, in *The Function of Reason*, points out that a limited conceptual framework, behaviorism for example, will be powerless to deal with dynamic issues.

In social psychiatry, the epidemiological interest was at

first not truly etiological in significance; it was restricted to searches for factors global enough to encompass social and psychological worlds, but unfortunately factors which were psychiatrically *unclear as to possible relevance*. These global determinants were, of course, the variations in socio-economic status, in urban and rural living, in cultural background, in ecological areas or neighborhoods of cities, in life-span mobility phenomena such as geographic or status mobility, etc. All such factors do, of course, influence personal *history*. Yet their adequacy in this generalized, and psychiatrically non-dynamic form remained questionable. Was economic deprivation in any sense the same as psychologically felt, conflictual deprivation? Were urbanites lonely in the sense that denizens of the "American Gothic" pattern were not? Did two-stage rises in upward mobility, as Ruesch and Bateson suggested, implement a sense of inadequacy and insecurity which was not dynamically there and operative already on grounds of personality structure? In addition to the mechanistic view of man *sub specie aeternitatis*, without cultural background, and the confusions of super-ego and sublimated cultural behavior "in the best of all possible worlds," there were failures to refine global notions of ecology in such a way that etiological and dynamic psychiatric questions could be tested and answered while attempting to draw epidemiological considerations and conclusions to the fore.

Considerations, such as Diethelm's of a variable typology, were lost in attempted intercorrelations of class with "schizophrenia" in general, "neuroses" in general, "depressive states" in general. The variable course of illness, dependent to so high a degree on neglect, or detection, proper diagnosis and treatment, could mean that high rates of schizophrenia in lower class groupings compared with high rates of neurosis in the upper classes might signify nothing more or less than variables in detection and treatment facilities and an unmitigated course of illness in the lower levels. As Diethelm indicates, the variables in environmental and cultural factors, all making for differences in psychopathology and change in personality expression according to situation and background factors were not adequately utilized in studies of this sort in epidemiological psychiatry. In brief, a combination of qualitative and quantitative methods was not devised in nosological nose-counting, such as might answer significant etiological questions.

In the social and psychological sciences likewise, loose conceptualizations traceable largely to ignorance of medical and psychiatric literature, failed to convince psychiatry of a rich field for study in socio-cultural backgrounds. At one time, not too long ago, texts on social "pathology," or social problems, ranged horrendous if well-meant statistics on economic poverty, broken homes, urban population density, class and minority group membership, etc., side by side with those on crime, delinquency, and psychiatric disorder to let the chips fall, or to comment ruefully on such unclear concepts as cultural "lag," the tempo of urban life, or the presumed inadequacies of the poor.

Modern concepts reveal no such shadow-boxing with remotely spaced variables like density and psychiatric disorders, or like poverty, crime and mental illness, least of all where mental disorder and anti-social behavior are confused. In a striking study, Dunham has recently indicated that the "quiet ones" of the slum area may be the ones most vulnerable to serious psychic disturbance, while open delinquent behavior in upper class homes may be the more patent indicators of underlying sociopathic trends. Again, etiology or illness process is considered directly in the context of an epidemiological problem. The tendency has been for involutional disorders to become more rare in modern times, and to have little of the sin and guilt ideology which was once so prevalent, for menopause to be less a point of depressive disorganization with changes in public attitude towards aging or towards sexual function in women and their social position. In the same way, the rarity of paranoid resultants of syphilitic infection due to anti-biotic discoveries and application; and a host of more subtle variations in mental illness course accompanying newer and more successful therapeutic methods; all point to etiological or developmental variants responsive to a whole range of environmental factors which have changed. The point that social and psychological analysis has not kept abreast of this changing scene is a reflection upon their slowness in adopting dynamic method.

As Diethelm notes in another source:[20]

> "Cultural anthropologic investigations are highly indicated for obtaining a clarification of the meaning of the changes in psychopathology. Ethnic influences have often been mentioned but have never been studied adequately. The role of religion in the incidence of suicide is well recognized but not understood. Cultural attitudes have affected sexual life. However, neglect of careful study has permitted the development of far reaching theories."

It is suggested that careful study, in this area of problems, is guided or informed by data which have psychodynamic relevance and psychopathological detail.

At the same time, social and psychological concepts have, in psychiatric and social science literature, undergone certain changes. The emergence of the Sullivan-Sapir position has already been mentioned. In respect to the factor of socio-economic status, Karen Horney, in an early work, *The Neurotic Personality of Our Time*, has made some general observations which may prove important. In place of the sheer effects of poverty on personality, Horney instead speaks of a high rate of neurosis throughout the entire social structure as the price paid for continual, unrelenting striving for success and prestige. Inevitably, the competitive pace throughout the whole socio-economic continuum loaded the circuit with private guilt and anxiety, as well as public uncertainty. The distance between aspiration levels and actual accomplishment when thrown upon this larger screen of generally accepted values was felt by many, if not all, as full of reproach and covert condemnation. For Horney, the individually focussed conflicts arose less out of infantile experience, as such, than from cultural reaffirmations of these values favoring neurotic attitudes, albeit traceable to family scene and large segments of life course. While non-neurotic fears of poverty or insecurity, situationally realistic and valid, existed in lower social classes and could be reality tested, character neuroses involved disproportionate fears, deeply rooted anxieties, and basic conflicts developed in part by cultural factors in the culture of our time. In place of the social pathologist's factor of poverty, a concept difficult to substantiate in other cultures such as the Bolivian Siriono, (described by Allan Holmberg as a hand to mouth existence amid uniform conditions of want and uniform survival ideals) Horney has suggested psychologically felt inadequacy and deprivation, rejection and anxiety.

Central to Horney's theory is that avoidances of anxiety are also unconsciously or consciously according to cultural formulae; drowning oneself in work or developing inordinate desires for power, prestige and possessions were plotted as sure routes to denying, domineering, humiliating or depriving conduct. Such defenses in these reaction formations as the boundless craving for affection, approval and admiration were, for Horney, not simply the occasional defenses of essentially isolated cases, but in the main larger cultural constructs, or values systems, than are found simply in the uncertainties of economic structure. What is striking is that such cultural themes are to be found where, most often, the real uncertainties are least apparent in the reality sense. Such additional cultural principles (V. F. Calverton once called them the cultural compulsives) as the constant need to emphasize sexual desirability, to develop a need for prestige so great that self-evaluation suffers in excessive reliance upon others, or to become self-assertive and aggressive in a manner that finds victims unable to protect themselves—these larger constructs were hammer and anvil of the anxieties and disproportionate fears, the culturally induced denials of their existence, the *psychological* reassurances against helplessness, humiliation and destitution. They could be found anywhere in social structure where unreasoning, competitive, hostile impulses and the culturally automatic need to suppress and repress them operated.

The cultural corollaries in showing off, in inordinate narcissistic desires, in fantasy dream factories, in the ease of projecting hostilities to an "outer" world, in cravings for power and self-justification, Horney saw not merely as a cartoon panorama of American foibles, but as serious failures in the America of our time. In writing of the reaction formations among those who succumbed, she emphasized the hostile submission and withdrawal, the enhanced and sensitive anxieties, the sense of inadequacy or guilt, and the countless defensive mechanisms against rejection. Whether the account is epidemiologically sound should be tested; at least it knows, etiologically and dynamically, what requires testing.

Just as the effects of poverty have given way to such analysis, or have, like Kardiner's study of the American urban Negro, explored the dimensions of hostility and deprivation together, so the factor of sheer population density, which once was a vogue of studies in the 1930's and 1940's best exemplified, perhaps, by Dunham and by Hyde, has given way in turn to more valid psychiatric

concepts.   Current concepts of urbanism have used the
famous Durkheimian notion of anomie in one form or
another.   It is important to know exactly what it means.
In the hands of Robert K. Merton, or in David Riesman's
The Lonely Crowd, anomie does not mean high density per
square mile nor even a kind of nondescript anonymity in
large groups.   It has no connotations of crowded tenement,
reprehensible though these may be on other grounds; nor
does it mean "the crowd" or *Carnival* setting.   Central to
the conception is a personally felt and generally conceived
sense of self-alienation from others.   If the tenement or
apartment house dwelling has thrown people together in
greater proximity, or the *Carnival* or *Mardi Gras* preserves
their anonymity, anomie separates them and imparts to
anonymity a crucial sense of lack of communication, lack
of indentity and lack of shared interests.

Increasingly, careful studies of urbanism have moved in
the direction of such concepts.   In one of the best delineated studies, that of Eshref Shevky and Marilyn Williams,
The Social Areas of Los Angeles, a comparison of urban process in this city and in others has disclosed that the process
is accompanied by increasing segregation, as of ethnic
minorities, differentiation of socio-economic areas, and in
fact greater homogeneity within areas or differentiation
between them, as the process wears on.   In relation to
anomie, the relation of the self-alienation process to that
of urbanism, social science concepts stressing size, cohesion
and types of social integration are relevant.   It is important
to know whether family and neighborhood oriented cultures, as perhaps the rural Puerto Rican or Southern Italian exemplify, limit belongingness more or less to such
units, or whether other substitutions from social structure
can be made for these frameworks.   Does the highly elaborated social structure and status system of the Hungarian
find parallels in the American status system, or does it

suffer attrition and lack of cohesion within the Hungarian community with little modification?

Are the ideas of Horney, or of Benedict, concerning psychological dislocations imbedded in our own Middletowns to be included in our own concepts of anomie?   At any rate, the shift to anomie from population density considerations, such as characterized Hyde's work in Boston, implies nothing less than a psychological reworking of social science concepts.   Instead of a populationally dense Transitional Zone, or Skid Row, being the class-linked matrix of the highest rates of schizophrenic illness, as it was considered in the early studies of Faris and Dunham, today the notion of downward mobility and selective "drift" of hitherto damaged personalities, as analyzed by Gerard and others, shows a pile-up, not an incidence rate, in this ecological area of those in whom the self-alienation course has possibly moved to full completion.[21]

In addition, minority or ethnic group membership no longer involves an insistence upon a unitary and cohesive cultural group, a fact which depends more upon the nature and reception of each specific sub-culture within the American scene.   The nature of the culture, together with the pace and type of acculturation change in the new setting are all of importance.   Today, before attempting to assess whether minority group members represent persons living in a hostile and alien world, as has been suggested in a brilliant manuscript on the development of paranoid personalities by J. S. Tyhurst, such factors as the psychological patterns of males and females within specific cultures, the intergeneration conflict or harmony, and the emotional climate of the typical "ethnic" home must first be known. Such data require not merely the recasting of psychiatric or anomie formulations in respect to foreign born, an important first step to be sure, but equally a careful analysis of self-alienation in separate and specific socio-cultural contexts with respect to the acculturation process and the changing scene. Until this is done, we shall not know whether we are dealing with alienation processes stressed by Horney for the entire urban American scene, or with socio-cultural factors of specific groupings in the population, or with economic hardship dimensions.

However, the step implied in the work of Tyhurst and Riesman, or of Merton or Gerard, a psychological working through of social science concepts, groups a lack of social cohesion and nonintegration together with self-alienation and depersonalization trends. As stated, such a reworking of general concepts must be tested in culturally distinct groups and patterns as indeed they were in Durkheim's original, brilliant work on contrasting backgrounds in *Le Suicide*.

In New York, for example, a content analysis of newspapers or an inspection of agency records will begin to describe a Puerto Rican family increasingly characterized by lack of cohesion, by struggles between parents (or parents and children) as to dominance role in a society in which male superiority was formerly unchallenged; the lesser subordination of the female in an urban scene of greater job opportunities for them; the resultant male and female role-conflicts; and the multiple common law marriages and separations; or in short, the central changes in family organization, child-rearing practices and intersexual conduct. The pace of this acculturation, the job instability for men, and the kinds and amount of personal insecurity and hostility are among the elements to consider.

As Leighton has suggested, interferences with satisfactions and security systems may foster psychological disorder. If this proposition is central in the study of environmental influence, and it appears to be, then specific kinds of interference may be connected with particular kinds of acculturation process. If further, in Puerto Rican cases which are known etiologically or dynamically, deprivation of maternal care, intersexual hostility, lack of masculine assertion among boys whose mothers compensate for absent father-figures or overprotect them in the formative years, are added to brittle marriages, floundering but not abandoned dual standards, and possibly infancy oral frustration, then a psychodynamic profile may emerge. While etiological, it will certainly relate to much of what is known epidemiologically to be striking in this group: the distillate of male fears of impotence, the psychosomatic stomach and digestive disorders, the high rates of homosexuality and prostitution, the frequent incest fears and male Oedipal conflicts. Consequently, a more coherent and dynamically valid pattern of explanation results than would by mere allusion to "alienation in a hostile world." The latter idea, while a clue, is really a circular explanation primarily because it does not begin with real people having, like all of us a cultural stock in trade, modified under certain conditions of acculturation and yet used under the conditions of time, place and specific circumstances.

Further on minority group phenomena, "the alien in a hostile world" represents a known quantity of decided epidemiological importance. The study of Barrabee at Boston Psychopathic Hospital has recognized this; Zborowski has re-emphasized it. In state hospitals and veterans' facilities, the numerical importance of such groups as German, Irish, Italian or Puerto Rican (depending of course on region) is striking. The number of first admissions to public psychiatric institutions has, since 1940, increased more than 28 per cent. This increase belongs to a period in which another half-billion outlay has been required for veterans' psychiatric needs. The figures, applying to native-born largely, do not argue that the problem of "hostility in an alien world" disappears with continued acculturation. Such study, as is required, cannot proceed on the basis of urban anonymity theory, but must include specific etiological and epidemiological inquiry. Only then could a causal nexus of specific group backgrounds and specific psychopathology become clear. Just as gross, or global, variables like socio-economic status, population density, and cultural background have undergone change and refinement, so the necessity of careful psychosocial studies, jointly guided by psychiatric and social science findings, demands a greater degree of specificity than is offered by such a breakdown of data into schizophrenias, psychoneuroses, and the like. Normative behavior and cultural background vary considerably from group to group. Presumably psychopathology can vary as well beyond such nosological labels as schizophrenic reaction, paranoid type.

This process of conceptual refinement must be made in psychiatry itself, if indeed, it stands to gain from social science collaboration. The readiness, in some quarters, for social sciences to dissolve concepts into those which have meaning and significance for psychiatry has already begun, even though the process has not been uniformly successful all along the line. In defining the specifics of psychopathology in relation to given conditions in social, cultural and environmental background no single science, whether social or psychiatric, has the analytic tools, or perhaps the time and inclination, to explore different modal reactions of human beings, as individuals and as members of groups, in physical, emotional and cultural dimensions. Yet the task must be begun against the background of enormous and sustained cultural forces which enter into behavior. Both in reference to epidemiology and etiology, the social scientist unaided has, to date, largely studied the non-biological homeostatic relationship of the individual with his total socio-cultural environment, the environment sometimes fragmentized for clarity in special problems.

In those elements which create disruptive or disorganizing tensions and anxieties, which block self-realization and self-consistency, the psychiatrist has his special province and unmatched competence. Where only an integration of sorts in a truly alien world remains, the psychiatrist alone has the skill to evaluate and explore, with caution and insight built up from clinical experience. To postpone or delay the psychiatrists' entry into and collaboration in this direction of critical socio-cultural *and* dynamic analysis is like saying, otherwise and all too philosophically, that because "society is the patient," to paraphrase L. K. Frank, therefore therapeutic and individualized efforts might just as well cease.

The sciences of man, like the sciences of his ills, must together investigate aspects of the human predicament if individualized therapy is to be linked with real progress in prevention, and in the alleviation of stressful situations. For the psychiatrist, as well as social scientist, this means that both individuals and their backgrounds may be studied and evaluated for strengths and weaknesses. In a truly epidemiological and preventive sense, the shattered lives of countless individuals and families require such fuller consideration. When the full force of human-related sciences attack the problems of psychiatric disorders in etiological and epidemiological research, then the results will be better, doubtlessly, for therapy and prevention.

The primary concern of psychiatry in the past, apart from typology and treatment, has been psychodynamic and etiological. In mental health research, the epidemiological approach, unfortunately, has too often been used alone. In much of this, statistics rather than individualized case analysis has meant that the distillate studied is removed many times from the original real product. In British social psychiatry, as in American, an effort has been made to recapture the reality of the individual in real situational contexts, just as this method informed the best work of Adolf Meyer and his associates. Neither method, the etiological or the epidemiological, can be used with any amount of assurance singly at any particular point. *How much* mental illness exists, or is produced in any society or culture within a time period depends on a series of conditions, among them the dynamic implications of specific ways of life.

As we shall see in the following sections on Prevalence and Incidence, and Multiple Causation *Versus* Single Factor Analysis, even more is contained in society and culture than primary way of life phenomena. Among these are the accuracy of methods for location and diagnosis of types of personality balance and imbalance. Suffice it to say here that in mental illnesses par excellence, the deeply rooted, insidious and slowly developing character of the disorders is especially noteworthy. If the schizophrenias account for a quarter of all those hospitalized, this probably means that both prevalence and incidence data may not be interpreted as in any sense final, unless early stages are capable of at least rough detection. In surveys of this sort, there is no reason why the institutional and expressive contexts of an individual, as a member of a family, community, society and culture, may not be searched provided the search remains psychiatric in essence.

THE INCIDENCE AND PREVALENCE OF PSYCHIATRIC DISORDERS

Prevalence and incidence studies, conducted in national and regional illness censuses, constitute one method of epidemiological survey. Although useless etiologically, they do have great practical importance in providing guidance of a general sort for over-all planning, public education in mental hygiene, and the assessment of mental ills in the total health and economy of the nation.   When H. Emerson, at the First International Congress on Mental Hygiene in 1930, gave gross quantitative evidence of the magnitude and extent of mental disorders as a public health problem and in the same decade outlined the first inclusive epidemiological research of this type, the movement was felt as a part of a long-overdue attack on the chronic, degenerative, crippling and neoplastic processes, more challenging and by this time more widespread and baffling than the germ-specific, mechanically isolatable, and pharmacologically treatable ailments.

Freeman, first in a number of epidemiological research innovations, stimulated in 1936 the first comprehensive survey in a major population of over 50,000 persons, the Eastern Health District of Baltimore.   This fieldwork was carried forward by Lemkau, Tietze and Cooper.   Then, in rapid succession, in 1938, there was the Williamson County, Tennessee survey of Roth and Luton, next the work of Dunham in Chicago, later Hyde in Boston, and Stott; along with these, there were the formal programs of incidence study in New York and Massachusetts.   The former were no doubt also influenced by Pollock's work in the 1920's, Nolan's in the decade before, and Malzberg's imposing surveys.

The two world wars, particularly World War II, gave decided impetus to studies of induction and rejection data, Hyde's mental rejection rates being wholly of this type. Subsequent studies of community population samples pushed beyond the frontiers established by Faris and Dunham, and the type of epidemiological team, now used, included the psychiatrist, anthropologist, sociologist, statistician, psychologist and social worker.   The German studies of Brugger in Thuringia and Bavaria, in the 1930's, and a host of Scandinavian studies; Stromgren's in Danish rural and fishing communities, Sjögren's and Böök's in Swedish villages and island districts, and Odegaard's of the Norwegian hospitalized antedated though mostly in rural circumstances the American urban and state surveys.

These studies are not comparable because of methodological differences in the gathering of data. Many of those in small Scandinavian fishing, farming and island districts adopted the method, since redeveloped in Leighton's study of Stirling County, Nova Scotia, of gathering extensive psychiatric information on known cases through fieldwork methods and with interested informants. With far less intensive methods and certainly less psychodiagnostic information, Brugger found a constantly higher rate in every illness category per 1,000 persons in Bavaria, as compared with Thuringia. The Tennessee Survey with its rate of 69.4 per 1,000, although rural, was no more reassuring than Paul Lemkau's data, roughly comparable but in an urban scene, with its figure of 60.5 per 1,000. The Dunham, Stott and Hyde studies, hardly comparable, tell at least a similar story of high rates, in no case pinpointed to the end result of being etiologically useful to dynamic psychiatry or psychotherapy. A study by R. M. Counts and Peter F. Regan, on Army recruits, has both dynamic and therapeutic meaning.[22]

A detailed study by Joseph Eaton and R. J. Weil of several Hutterite communities described a variant culture of the United States and Canada possessing great stability and conservatism in social pattern, decided moral and religious emphasis, a distinct limiting of individualistic and impulsive tendencies, and considerable constriction in emotional expression. While this population had a seemingly higher than average occurrence of "manic-depressive disorders," the "lifetime prevalence rate" used in this study, and compared with the non-uniform methods and results obtained in Germany, Scandinavia and elsewhere remains open to serious question; if intended for comparison with incidence rates from other settings, it must be computed for incidence and not prevalence. Further, a "lifetime prevalence rate" if not made age-specific by information as to probable age of onset is especially vulnerable in application to what Eaton terms "manic-depressive disorders" in view of an age-distribution for this illness generally older than schizophrenias. In fact, no pattern of cultural etiology may be assumed until the age pattern of Hutterite communities, generally regarded as skewed in an elderly direction, is made manifest, and until a rate of incidence is computed in a time period for these communities commensurate with known information on the age distribution in this population.[23]

It is obvious that *how much* mental illness exists or is produced in any society or culture within a given time period depends upon a series of conditions implicit in that setting. A methodology, however, by its definitions of illness, and by its means of locating, detecting, and diagnosing illness interposes a new series of conditions between the reality of prevalence or incidence and the findings of the study. Here it must be remembered that chronic, degenerative or psychic diseases often develop slowly, and that for those ill the continuum of the illness state, like the life span itself, is in truth a lengthy continuum. Detection and diagnosis is one problem to be sure, but it is a problem complicated by the sheer presence or absence of treatment. Facilities for treatment, or exacerbation by neglect, may go far to explain the striking findings of Redlich, Hollingshead and Myers in the New Haven Study, a survey in which lower class members showed 12 times the amount of schizophrenic illness as the upper class, for whom in turn the rates of psychoneurosis were distinctly higher.[24] The fact that a survey, for a given day, of those known to private psychiatrists and to public hospitals and clinics forms the basis for these findings supports this interpretation.

Moreover, an incidence rate of *new cases occurring* in a time period, much less open to secondary questions of treatment or neglect, must be age and sex specified, not merely denoted as to class and culture. The age and sex patterns of illnesses are remarkably subject to change in time and correspondence with socio-cultural factors, of which more will be said later. Even an incidence rate, age and sex specified, will depend to some extent on attitudes towards illness and community or family modes of detection.

While the folklore of mental illness is hardly explored as yet, anyone knows that the Italian attitude towards expression of feelings directly, their dislike of introspection, and their great familial concern lest illness be detected in the family created a set of conditions quite unlike the English or "Yankee" attitude towards hospitals, clinics and individual therapeutic skills and facilities. These attitudes towards illness and treatment, modes of detection, and the presence or absence of facilities are present in any social grouping. Unlike the germ-specific diseases, for which incidence rates provide the most direct kinds of etiological clues, mental disorders as a life course process are less responsive to computation, inference and control group procedures such as served Semmelweis' discovery of specific etiological agents in puerperal fever.

However, since prevalence rates merely compound and add the piled up and time-bounded rates of incidence, they offer no recourse in method. Indeed, age and sex specific rates, if computed by incidence data alone, give more insight into the life course process of disease. The prevalence rates have merely the uses of administrative survey into present extent of a series of illness problems, which presumably grow and pile up under the rubrics of neglect, custodial care, or failure in treatment. Such indeed, is the value of the Faris and Dunham study of Chicago's Transitional Zone in which neglect and piling up of existing cases both occurred. Whereas, an epidemiological survey which can obtain incidence data and a measure of personal and biographical history for each individual has further uses.

The growing recognition of a gap, therefore, between "true incidence" and currently ascertainable incidence reported without a history of illness points not only to the serious import of case-finding in the community and institutionally (and possibly in the former area, preventive or "early" therapeutic methods), but it suggests again that such approximate epidemiological methods as are available in this field be linked with etiological knowledge and understanding. As we have seen, *how much* mental illness occurs in given social and cultural groups depends ultimately on processes best called etiological and answering the questions *how* and *why*. At the same time epidemiology, if careful, provides clues to how and why, baselines for research into further etiological questions, and if linked with prevalence studies in modern communities, some knowledge for the planning of mental health resources, preventive measures, educational and therapeutic programs.

From the point of view of mental hygiene and preventive psychiatry, the ambulatory ill and borderline cases (those for example with incipient schizophrenia, mild neurotic or psychosomatic symptoms) are of considerable importance both for therapy and mitigating educational programs. The National Mental Health Act appropriations for state aid are entirely for such purposes, and yet little knowledge of real needs in this area exists at present. While the occurrence of early symptoms among people is certainly not the same as the fuller study of disease processes, whatever factors have a bearing upon incidence are etiologically interesting. In this sense, there is better conformance to the actual meaning of incidence when applied to "early stages" of slowly developing and insidious disease processes. For incidence is the appearance of a disease entity in populations both as to distinct and clear prodromal symptoms, as well as the final occurrence and distribution of its ultimate states. Such distributions, graded or evaluated as to seriousness, are computed as to rates of appearance. If then, certain psychiatric disorders have an early development, as indeed they appear to have, the age specific data together with the noting of a course of illness will come closer to real incidence.

Further, new disease occurrences may be evaluated against the background of such larger distribution patterns as have implicit in them the failure to arrest the course of illness, or its continuity, exacerbation or worsening, or even partial cure and temporary remission. The discussions of Hoch, Polatin and others on the possibly dubious entity, pseudoneurotic schizophrenia, and the whole question of its distinctness as an entity *versus* its linkage or intermediacy between two processes could benefit immensely from such refined statistical analysis. Where, as in mental illness, there exist deeply significant differences between psychotic manifestations in which ego control and integration are lost, and neuroses in which they are retained with discomfort, considerable care must be exercised to distinguish these gradients and not to confuse or blur them with the still larger groupings as the mentally ill and sociopathic "in general." In the same way, psychodynamic and psychopathological information should correct the confusions common in epidemiological and incidence data now reported. Who has not pondered over reports where mere parts of larger disease processes (such as "chronic alcoholism," the neurotic, sociopathic or psychotic delinquent, and non-genetic types of mental deficiency) are grouped erroneously and stud the epidemiological surveys of Europe, America and Africa? In his study of alcoholism, Diethelm has suggested just such a correction.[25]

Felix and Bowers have therefore singled out two types of factors relevant to incidence rates, the first being the knowledge of etiology or how persons acquire the disorder, and the second, knowledge of methods to combat it plus the possibilities of their application in given communities and settings. The methods of casefinding, psychodynamic development, choices of therapeutic method, cultural "safety valves" and preventive programs therefore have immediate bearing upon incidence and all respond to socio-environmental factors.[26] In a paper on *Prognosis in the Psychoneuroses: Benign and Malignant Developments*, Rennie states, "Much depends upon the character or temperament, the nature and duration of pathological defenses, the intrinsic ego strength of the individual and the many modifiable or unmodifiable environmental realities which the patient must surmount . . ." Later he adds, "As Saul has pointed out, neuroses are not entities. They are ways of reacting which everyone has in some degree. Even the most 'normal' individual utilizes similar mechanisms, however rudimentary, whenever the conflicts of inner needs or the strains of life are heightened." Considering his twenty year follow-up study of 240 hospital-treated psychoneurotic patients, Rennie concludes in part:[27]

" . . . Psychoneurosis is not a specific disease entity but is a method of reacting. The clinical manifestations frequently overlap so that one can see the utilization of many kinds of defense mechanisms in a given individual. The defense mechanisms which give the clinical coloring to the particular reaction are ones which are common to everyone and are significant largely because of the degree and extent of their use by the psychoneurotic person. Such defenses may and often do change either as an immediate result of therapy or as a spontaneous evolution subsequent to therapy . . . Most cases present admixtures. The essential task is to understand what and how the mechanisms operate and in what kind of setting in terms of character organization. While the long term outcome for most psychoneurotic patients following treatment is a benign one, the development of malignant states occurs in a sufficient number of patients to call for special alertness in the diagnosis, prognosis and choice of therapy for every psychoneurotic patient."

The studies of incidence of psychiatric disorders have been generally, of three types both here and abroad. These are, first, the national and state surveys mentioned above. There are next the studies of institutionalized cases as to number, not etiology or follow-up phenomena, which have been centered largely in public agencies, often state hospitals, and consequently deal for the most part with psychotics. While the Scandinavian studies, the Stirling Project in Nova Scotia, the New Haven study, or the Yorkville Community Mental Health Project broaden case-finding to include all known ambulatory and institutional cases under treatment, those based on admissions rates in public institutions show decided incompleteness of data because only obvious psychotics are selected into the study, and, at times, even the private institutional and out-patient clinic data are excluded. The Scandinavian method of using informants and scattered sources of data to expand this picture is methodologically loose and unsystematic. Until the continuum of neurotic to psychotic manifestations is utilized and the community as well as institutional scene probed by multidisciplinary methods, there is no assurance that an area has been studied from a rounded epidemiological point of view. There are no short cuts in epidemiology which may successfully eliminate the field survey, statistical study of mass phenomena, and institutional cases, public and private.

There is decided point, however, to the study within hospital settings of remission rates in response to modern methods of treatment, provided a full knowledge of both therapeutic handling and disease course has been attained. In ordering a jumble of data which may otherwise mean little, first admissions, age, sex, social and cultural data together with psychodynamic data comprise leading considerations against which style of therapy and remissions may be significant.

In psychiatry, there is increasing appreciation that epidemiology in mental disorders, the reaction patterns themselves, are rarely responsive to single agents, internal or external, for which specifics in prevention or in therapy singly apply. Notions of "precipitating events" are never active in isolation from the totality of a patient's patterns of reacting or the totality of the situation in terms of which he reacts; etiologically, the traumatic and precipitating factors, sometimes called predisposing, are to be referred to the basic facts of types of personality, the manner in which they develop, and the kinds of backgrounds responsible for such development.

The homeostatic and disequilibrium theories apply with special force only if one realizes that the only homeostasis, or lack of it, which can exist is contained in the total contours of personality, built from and operating within contexts. In anthropological experience, traumatic events and shamanistic cures, especially for hysterias, will stand as mere anecdote and vignette against the larger analysis of character, and temperament and reaction to situation. In psychiatric literature, the character neurosis with hysterical features often runs parallel so that grief reactions as in death of a close family member may mean not situationally realistic sorrow, but personally felt defeat and psychic illness, as both Lindemann and Volkart have recently pointed out. The searing and ghastly experiences which a healthy personality may meet, feel, and take in stride are proof enough that trauma, experienced by a number of personalities, will take no toll except in given configurations.   Thus, hypotheses which postulate that categories of deprivation (death, want, class-necessitated job mobility, "traumatic" weaning or toilet training, etc.) are predisposing and relate to incidence of disorder are clinically assumptive and no amount of quantification, apart from distinctly known cases, can convince one that remote variables are not being manipulated.   Sunspots are simply not correlated with economic cycle, though relation of such items has been assumed.   The factors with which incidence rates are connected must be, on independent grounds, found to be dynamically important.

The world is full of cultures in which relatives and close associates die; it is full of cultures with hand-to-mouth marginality in which most frequently the poorer, unacculturated communities show the more optimum mental health; there are cultures like our own in which job instability in the blue collar range is often a matter of economic instabilities and periodicities and not a personal determination; and there are cultures which wean more abruptly than the Anglo-American, and yet do not have our problems of high incidence in the least.   In the cities of Australia and New Zealand abrupt toilet-training and weaning seem to have no reflection in illness rates.

Just as single agents, "precipitating" and "traumatic" events require further clarification in the methodology of studies of the incidence of nonorganic mental illness, so new hypotheses setting more exact parameters of the problems are required in research design intending to use the interrelational concepts of social psychiatry. The precipitating event and predisposing factor has been used to illustrate the narrowest constriction of such parameters.   However, the theory of the functioning psychosocial unit, now generally accepted as a frame of reference, needs further specification, particularly as to functioning, in order to escape vapid over-generalization. To prevent the scope of the problem from becoming too wide and general, the extremely stimulating Sullivan-Sapir theory of the emotional and expressive quality of human symbolic communication must be tested for limits.

This theory, to be applied at all, necessitates more than the generous attributing now prevalent of these positive and sensitizing qualities to the pan-human species without qualification. As Lasswell, who had much to do with originating and elaborating communication theory, pointed out recently at the Mass Communications Seminar of the Wenner-Gren Foundation for Anthropological Research, it is of utmost importance to note in the general theory of communication the place of this process *in* the social process.[28] One might add *within* the values systems *of* the social process. He needs only to ask *what* is being communicated, and *why?*

The psychiatrist, accustomed to study a personality as a whole in relation to interactions with others, frequently denotes the conditioned or habitualized stamping into the soma and personality of emotional voltages, circuits and blocked circuits that finally characterize the economy and balance of the expressive life. The social scientist, particularly the anthropologist, by much the same process of evaluative entering into the affective, expressive and structured activities of groups of people and their generalized patterns of interaction explores to a similar depth, though rarely organically (unless a physical anthropologist) the symbol-charged, communicative mileu into which he has entered. The total personality and total cultural approaches, in each realm, impose similar conditions in which affective dimensions in either loom large. Beyond the affectivity, the social conditions of existence are present in either case, whether material, ideological, or traditional. No matter how idiosyncratic and individualized the psychopathology may become, it links back at some point as do the lonely trails to more generalized routes.

In each realm, the similar conditions of the problems are: What, specifically, has been communicated and how? What values and attitudes determine the affect? What expressive symbolism has been utilized, and why? The organic and individual biological need basis of the one frame, and the historical or evolutionary and bio-social need basis of the second or cultural framework need not blind us, beyond noting the difference in numbers and in emphasis (the "ill" or "well") to the essential concern with *specified* communication processes. The varying and definable differences in values systems, roles, aspirations, and culturally determined strengths and weaknesses are still there. In either case there are constant and special problems of adaptation to milieu and characteristic methods of attempting to achieve homeostasis.

While conceivably too, whole culture groups and social classes function materially (feeding, clothing, housing and functioning in productive systems), or provide a modicum of recreation, relaxation or harnessing of energies, or organize social and sexual life, etc., our ability to learn about these functions, or psychotic distortions of them, is still dependent on these same processes of symbolic communication within structured systems. Terms like communication, adjustment, transmission of tradition, or emotional expressivity are meaningless without concretization, specification as to structures like culture or class as well as function, and a typology which indicates what is communicated, adjustment to what, passive transmission of which tradition, or emotional expressivity with what values and actions at stake.

In the same manner, mechanistic terms like projection,

repression, sublimation or regression require structural as well as functional referents, even as does the richly qualified and quantified world of mental illness in which raw hostility, tension, anxiety, displacement, distortion, hallucination, withdrawal and isolation, fear, panic, apprehension, or guilt may play a role. The indentification or non-identification or misidentification patterns so important in establishing or losing ego controls function only in self-other configurations, as George H. Mead so cogently demonstrated. There are, in actuality, no genuine regressions and total withdrawals, nor can there be in self-other relational systems. The pertinent and differing amounts of ego-strength or reality tested self-reference can only be spelled out, as to emergence, by an individual's actual points of reference, to parents of same or opposite sex, parent surrogates, siblings, males, females, to people, toward cultural events and typical occurrences that mark a life course and are laden with meaning.

The fact that humans can learn to use systems of symbols and be conditioned to them swells the world of meaning far beyond the mere mammalian level of learning by signs, signals and concrete perceptions. But it promotes the less objectified universe, the gross irrationalities, and, with equal bestowal of the gifts of art, language, science and philosophy, the nonrational use and interpretation of environment, the uncommunicative nonsense, the scourge of war or blight of insanity. To enter into study of these differentials, ethically varying at base, the psychosocial position must qualify and quantify within the social system the strains and stresses that produce these last emergents, in the same sense and on the same levels of interest and valuation that psychiatry utilizes in determining degrees of ego loss, gain and asset.

This means, in either case, that thought and action in human and cultural dimensions may be measured qualitatively in terms of function and typology, provided specific conditions of culture, class or personality balance are understood as dynamic processes. If for example, displacements and misidentifications or recognitions and warm relationships characterize an adjustment; or to use Sullivan terminology, if "good-me," "bad-me" or "not-me" constellations, male or female, are developed within a milieu, both the milieu and the resultant constellation must be viewed as related and dealt with as "incidence" or emergents. The only point at which the connected series must be watched with utmost care, in view of the spare adjustive machinery and natural, compensatory mechanisms of all men, is in the endless safety valves of cultural systems and in the safe-guarding play of adjustive (and protective) mechanisms within the individual.

The uniqueness of events, individuals, and cultural systems may prevent complete determinacy or one-to-one correlates between cultural stress systems and personality breakdown, and mathematical precision or perfection may be statistically unwarranted. Nevertheless, indications of relationship between the cultural environment and pathology are fully as expectable from carefully guided studies of incidence, as is the endless documentation already achieved from studies of normative, cultural behavior, class variations and their ego-involvements in anthropology, sociology and social psychology.

In summary, of the three general methods of medicine about which knowledge of disease processes can be built—the clinical study of individual patients, laboratory experiment, and the epidemiological approach of field and statistical studies of disease processes in groups of people, psychiatry has achieved its major successes only in the first two areas. The potential of the last method to contribute, particularly where the knowledge gained has more general capacity to be turned to good effect in therapeutic practice, management, control, education and prevention, is incalculable at the present time. It has been used, somewhat gingerly, and in limited scope in such therapies as the group psychotherapy session where at present the consensus as to optimum number of small group relationships that can be handled hovers about the eight-person mark; it has been used, no doubt unconsciously, in occupational and other push-therapies, in mass educational media like the film, television and radio, in child guidance and community clinics, in trusteeship and privilege systems of larger institutions, and in recreational and self-government experimentation, supervised of course, in the smaller. In the English Borstal system for delinquency as reported by Healy and the social psychiatry methods of Belmont, reported by Maxwell Jones, using psycho-drama, group therapy sessions and carefully tested community methods of re-education, have the implications of an epidemiological approach gone furthest.[29]

But nowhere, to our knowledge, has the epidemiological method, involving cultural study in urban settings, been used first as a method of research and then applied with the perspective of "cultural push-therapy" in mind. In all this, the first aim must be to see how existing techniques for mass measurement of psychiatric disorder may be enlarged and adapted in biological, psychological and social dimensions, and next to consider their possible use in the more delicate and practical problems of therapy, control and prevention.

In view of the vast range and variation of individual mental disorders and the complexity or indefiniteness of symptomatic syndromes and subtypes, a further qualification must be added to the etiological usefulness of the kinds of surveys which are not guided by clinical, psychodynamic and socio-cultural inquiry. We have already stated that studies which reveal putative or apparent incidence rates, however approximate, may be estimating how much malfunction can exist or pile up within specific socio-cultural groups, but that they do not in this form answer the how and why of malfunction or adjustment. For this reason, research psychiatry has divided into two wings, unfortunately not always again brought into relationship. That which surveys and aggregates general statistical ranges is forced repeatedly to retreat from even the most general etiological questions. The other, dealing with specific cases and their psychodynamic and therapeutic involvements concerns single patients and nonsignificant series. No doubt, as we have seen, the statistics have partial usefulness, and the patient-formulations considerable practical importance.

But because the processes never link systematically with findings on a given backgrounded area, the repetition of surveys marks no adaptation to actual research needs in diagnostics, therapy or prevention. The continued analyses of patients must continue to have the clinical ring of a private office, of limited discovery and of lack of research consolidation of net gains. Science has always more general, incisive and inclusive concerns and methods. The limited scope of each monotonously disparate study, the one microscopic and particularized, the other quantified, but etiologically limited, suggests that only a combination of methods, the full battery of medical research methodology, applied to a given, known socio-cultural area can deliver any fresh results or prevent the current and scattered dissipations of effort.

In personality formation, or even in its repressive or dissociative processes (whether we are dealing primarily with parent-child, sibling, peer group, intersexual or status group relations, or with the values, attitudes, meanings and motivations associated with such relationships) these all vary with class and culture, with degree or pace of acculturation, or, in short, with the kinds of systems of human symbolic communication and activity set up in the first instance within a culture. It is this normative pattern of meanings and activities to which the research methods called clinical and those called epidemiological must both make reference. Without it, the psychodynamic and genetic approach of the Freudian movement and its successors has functional insights into personality without structural points of reference, whereas the various environmentalist and physiological schools, stemming from the pioneer work of Adolf Meyer, have the needed environmentalist emphases corrective of the early descriptive and experimental movements fostered by Kraepelin and Bleuler, without denoting accurately the variables in socio-cultural experience that finally account for details of both structure *and* function in personality. It is this latter detail which Rennie suggests "should give us increasingly concrete data for preventive psychiatry and public mental health programs."[30] In research operation, it requires an accommodation, if not a fusion, of various social, medical and psychological researches into a new form of multidisciplinary, social psychiatric research. In research perspective, it necessitates an awareness, new to our times, that the individual and his peers may be studied in both functional-organic and functional-behavioral dimensions as a member of a family, community, neighborhood, status group and culture. These last-mentioned structural referents of systems of personality are themselves dynamic or variable in operation so that their description, for these purposes, must again be made in terms of structures, functions, meanings and values and the impact these have, of necessity, upon the dynamics of personality.

In ethnologic studies, aside from such classics as Junod's BaThonga, the Chukchi of Bogoras and a dozen others, the older penchant for describing the cultural world under bare bones of social organization, economics, ritual and belief with material and social culture neatly pigeonholed and ordered under fragmented headings has long since passed away. The cultural anthropologist now leaves room for life span, for basic values and emotional expressivity, for social process, dynamic change or acculturation, and the newer rubrics of child care, economic process, status system and functional interpretations of religion. There are even psychological studies of political system, folklore and drama, art, music and belief. The methods now extant and involving a re-creation of life ways are precisely those usable to dynamic psychiatry.

Psychiatrists work empirically with just this type of data in reference to specific cases, but unlike social scientists, do not usually formulate general interrelations between cultures and personalities. The exceptions to this rule comprise a long and growing list including such names as Jung and Rank, Rado, Ferenczi and Róheim, Horney, Kardiner, Sullivan and Thompson, Diethelm, Rennie, Ruesch, Levy, Lin, Yap, Dhunjibhoy, Stainbrook, Morita, Carothers, Böök, Bergler, Murray, Joseph, Lindemann, Leighton, and to an extent in their day, even Kraepelin and Bleuler. In cultural anthropology, the contrasts among ethnic groups are vivid and dramatic particularly if one ranges across regional and continental boundaries without benefit of a cultural typology or historical frames of reference. Less because the contrasts were germane to the contemporary Western world and more because they documented man's emotional life, the psychoanalytic movement drew closer to anthropological materials than any other field within psychiatry to an extent of making the literature of the two fields at times indistinguishable. Among the famous historical collaborations of just the last two decades, one could mention the work of E. H. Erikson with A. L. Kroeber and Scudder Mekeel, of Harry Stack

Sullivan with Edward Sapir, of the Leightons with Clyde Kluckholn, Kardiner with Linton and DuBois, Redlich or Babcock and Caudill, Ruesch and Bateson, Joseph and Spicer, Lindemann and the Parsons group. As Kluckhohn points out in *One Hundred Years of American Psychiatry*, edited by J. K. Hall, Zilboorg and Bunker in 1944, a summary of these and other associations discloses that cultural anthropology was most usually to be found, until recently, in the modified psychoanalytic wings of psychiatry. Brill's studies among the Eskimo before 1920, Coriat's among the Yahgan, and Róheim's extensive fieldwork were merely historical forerunners of what increasingly has been the case.

Yet cultures, and the human psychological processes contained within them, vary sufficiently so that human patterns of thought, motivation, learning process, characteristic activities and emotional expression cannot be considered as uniform introjected patterns. Conversely, the adult personality dynamics of the human species, and the rough similarity if not indentity of the human learning process anywhere make it unlikely that in culture and psychology "anything may happen." This means that a style of weaning or a mode of achieving sphincter control, as isolated and independent features of a culture, will not predetermine adult personality configurations. In any real sense of personality dynamics in the total life course, it is far more likely that the cultural attitudes towards infancy and childhood, its kinship setting, and the values of human individual worth will affect the infancy handling and disciplines, the parental behavior and the family functioning.

In a manner only unconsciously explored in anthropology and underwritten in its literature, the predominant ethical patterns and values, the conceptions of health, the meeting of individual needs throughout life span are prob-

ably the general determinants of kinds of personality encountered in a social scene. While such points seem logically patent, it is still a far cry and a crucial step for psychiatry to translate these into the language of emotional
health and illness, to find them operating in the economy
of personality, and to locate such profiles translatable into
incidence and prevalence.

It is, nevertheless, at this point that case sampling is
needed according to socio-cultural background to provide
life histories in known matrices, and further contrasts
through the study of the well and ill in each society. At
this point, also, both the methods of cultural anthropology
and social psychiatry must be used, now one and now
another in scientific demonstration, if an adequate social
psychiatry is to be developed. Therefore, psychological
mechanisms may be studied in relation to case situations,
and the histories of normal and ill, within a sample and in
a context of the cultural realities affecting patients and
respondents.

Secondly, the definition of a case may, for such etiological and incidence study, include any persons in the normal-
abnormal continuum. It is important, in addition, to
study sex and family role differentia, intergeneration conflict, and identification processes. In seeking out such
relationships, one may measure them against cultural
backgrounds and situations, matching the well and ill by
such factors as sex and age, family role and cultural
experience.

We are led, finally, to a series of distinct and definite
methodological conclusions by our consideration of prevalence and incidence study. While careful incidence studies
represent a vast advance over those of prevalence, they
cannot, in the research on mental disorder, take the place
of psychogenetic and psychodynamic studies. Put differently, neither the psychogenetic nor the epidemiological

approaches meet the requirements of etiological knowledge when used singly. When used together, the first to provide a rounded verification of psychiatrically valid hypotheses, and the second to test statistically the hypotheses concerning groups of people, the combined methods of research may yield the kind of data which withdraws support from competing explanations and really withstands rigorous scrutiny.

Before such studies are put into actual operation, however, a second corollary or principle must be used to provide the frame of reference for both types of inquiry just noted. In brief form, such a corollary states that the social and cultural referents of behavioral functioning, whether in those well or those ill, are the dynamically most relevant factors in socio-cultural environment. These last are not just class and cultural labels applied loosely, but the dynamically repeated, emotionally charged, typical and thematic values of a culture which become reflected, unconsciously at times, into the dynamic, behavioral processes of individuals. Cultures will, of course, vary in the degree to which they permit or promote ease, naturalness and positive development in interpersonal communication. In general, it is postulated that the greater the amount of intercommunication on this positive level, the greater the amount of functional good health.

While good mental health and good human relations are almost interchangeable terms, as Thomas Ling, in England, has pointed out, there are no doubt other elements.[31] Spontaneity (in the sense used above, of ease, naturalness and freedom in interpersonal communication), security and confidence, creativity and other terms have all been used to describe positive and beneficial mental functioning. However welcome such individually-centered definitions have been in clarifying kinds of emotional experience, they fail in not defining well and ill within known cultural frameworks.

Erich Fromm, both in *Escape From Freedom* and *Man For Himself*, has expressed the dilemma by which terms like "normal" or "healthy" may mean quite different things. From the point of view of the functioning society, fulfilling the social role or roles one takes, or participation in social productivity and social reproduction constitutes normalcy or health; whereas from the individual standpoint the optimum of individual growth and happiness marks this result. In this view, creativity, spontaneity, freedom, productivity and expression of one's highest potentialities are selected as the aims of mental hygiene. Indeed, in one sense they are. But the error of Fromm, or the dilemma he does not wholly solve, is implicit in the failure to analyze dynamic processes as parts of recognizable social situations or "fields" of cultural influence.[32]

In this sense, one may choose between the two great traditions which have directed man's thinking about himself, the Artistotelian which holds that the behavior of all things is determined by their nature (and which might posit individual urges for freedom, creativity and spontaneity) and the Galilean tradition which holds that the behavior of all things is determined by the conditions under which it occurs. Dynamic processes as opposed to more static attributes or entities; or the behavior of people in response to specific situations, rather than as expressions of attributes "possessed by human organisms," is the course we favor. It is classical psychiatry and prescientific anthropology which both spoke descriptively, and rarely analytically, of organic attributes, excluded environmental influence, denoted racial entities, delineated the "unit psychosis," described invariant typologies whether in illness or in culture, and failed to discover process or contextual referents anywhere. If human behavior is ability to communicate on symbolic and conceptual levels, then the systems of communication, whether disordered or not, have reference to symbolic, conceptualized values systems. Freedom, creativity and sponteneity do not exist *sub specie aeternitatis* any more than does mankind.   There are always the conditions of existence, modifying existence.   Culture, human values and psychiatric resultants may be more closely linked in real cultural systems than the men of any one of them have ever dreamed.   And of course the relativity of cultures, one to another, is always open to human modification.

II

THE DIMENSIONS OF CULTURE
AND HUMAN VALUES

CULTURE AND PERSONALITY AS RELATED SYSTEMS:
MULTIPLE CAUSATION

PSYCHIATRISTS increasingly recognize that epidemiology of mental disorders is something more than public health detective work, designed to ferret out the factors responsible for specific diseases with the purpose of applying controls and preventive measures against their action. Epidemiologists, through association with medical historians, psychiatrists, social scientists and psychologists, are obtaining clearer understanding of group characteristics of mental diseases.

At one time, rural communities were held to be homogeneous, imposing codes and customs, involving neighbors in personal crises, and with less *anomie* presumptively, producing less personal maladjustment. The mechanization of agriculture, the increased means of communication and the virtual disappearance of the hinterland dividing city and farm did little to dispel the popular assumption that the tempo of city life, its alleged lack of neighborhood, community, and kinship connections exposed the individual to a weakened family and institutional support and control, and consequent instability.

On second thought, no one thought seriously that the "tempo of urban life," as such, had any psychiatric meaning, that urban Irish from rural countryman backgrounds turned secular, that upper status groups in the largest cities had any great rates of residential mobility, that urban neighbors were always more remote than rural ones, or that acculturation of American ethnic groups meant in the least a "melting pot" of nondescript, cultureless anonymity.   As Canon Michael Shannon, an Irish priest from abroad, recently remarked at a New York Irish Feis, "The Irish in the U.S. are more Irish than those in Ireland."

The studies of Lemert in Michigan, covering five years' admissions to state and private hospitals, and analyzed not only for counties and regions, urban and rural, but within individual counties for place of provenience, show the thinly populated fishing, mining and resort counties of the Upper Peninsula to have the highest mental illness rates (80.6 per year per 100,000), the southern agricultural counties to come next (67.5), the urban southern areas next (66.2) and the marginal forest and farming areas, last.[33] Not merely Lemert, and possibly Eaton and Weil's data on the Hutterites, have thrown doubt upon the claim that rural communities are havens of mental health, but the classic study of Roth and Luton in the Williamson County rural area of Tennessee based on house-to-house field survey showed a total of mental incapacitation of 69.4 per 1,000 in 1938 far larger than the Baltimore Survey of Lemkau, Tietze and Cooper (1936) with its total for active cases of 60.5.[34]   Mangus in Butler County, Ohio, found that differences in urban, village, and farm population rates of children's personality adjustment did not favor any of the three groups considered.[35] Leland Stott's research on intellectual and mental adjustments of urban and rural children in Nebraska pointed in the same direction.[36] In brief, by 1950, epidemiological psychiatry already knew something of the lack of clear differentiation in the incidence of mental illnesses as a whole in urban or rural settings.   In some cultural configurations, rural maladjustment rates far exceeded the urban.   From the point of view of the psychic economy and emotional life of these areas, little was known, anthropologically or psychologically, of the effects of the social and affective family settings, of the values, of different family structures, or of community organization in each case.

The presence, in the Baltimore study of Lemkau, Tietze and Cooper, of groupings like Czechs, Jewish and Negro, in contrast to the way of life of rural Tennesseans, was not analyzed in anthropological field survey to test for relevant differences. As concerns the process of urbanism in connection with the Baltimore survey, it can only be repeated that Shevky, Williams and others determined this process to be one in which more or less segregated cultural enclaves or communities tend to form into status-differentiated and ethnically delineated sets of units as the process wears on.

As Emerson noted in 1939, we have incidence rates "without any environmental counterparts to our information and . . . exquisite vignettes of individual cases without enough of them to paint a picture of the composite." In addition to having the "environmental counterparts" brought up to date with current social theory and epidemiological information, "the vignettes of individual cases" must be made consistent with modern psychiatric science. Emerson's "composite picture" is obtainable only when culture, social group and personality are studied in actual relationship, and when, as in control group studies in medical research, samples of well and ill are matched within a series that equalizes (or holds constant) each factor in turn. Sub-studies of demoralization, mass hysterias, delinquency, or suicide, where applicable, are possible within the same framework. Before this can be done, studies which consider background factors must locate sample populations with sufficient status and cultural contrasts in large enough quantities to determine age, sex, status and cultural difference. Determinations to analyze status, but not culture, or to study cultures and sub-cultures without status variations, or equally to fail to reach agreement on the necessity of considering only *the combined effects of both together* are all three, as methods, doomed to failure. If culture, status and personality are related systems, they are always relational and must be studied in combination. There are no statuses without cultural underpinnings. There are probably few American urban sub-cultures without status and role differentiation.

In a cogent article, "In Defense of Culture-Personality Studies," J. W. Eaton has suggested there is no Single Factor explanation of personality, that ordinarily experiences need frequent and consistent repetition to become emotionally meaningful, and that the child must experience personally or be aware of normal standards in reference to self-judgments.[37]   Even so, statistical assessments of the effects of cultural practices are rough approximations of probability extremely valuable for the psychiatrist to possess, to be sure, since his whole science in the nature of the case is founded upon the same approximate foundations of probability.

Yet only 13 years before, in the same journal, *The American Sociological Review*, and with culture-personality studies in their infancy, J. W. Woodard, in his article, "The Relation of Personality Structure to the Structure of Culture," was relating the Freudian doctrine of a super-ego to the "control culture" or Weltanschauung of a people as a whole and unfortunately drawing the analogy down, in what is now outmoded sociology and psychiatry, to fixed processes of "psychotic dissociation" always connected with that extremely nebulous concept of "social disorganization."[38]   The notion of fixed processes of "social disorganization" to accommodate similar fixed notions of psychological disintegration is today even more debatable in the light of figures, from England, on the diminution of neuroses in those areas most subject to conditions of severe air raid bombings in World War II.

However, the German Descriptive Schools of psychiatry, of Kraepelin, Ziehen and Wernicke which were dominant just after the turn of the century, and which provided the first adequate observational material for the Western world, persisted in the description of fixed entities and a fixed progression in illnesses. Zilboorg, in his historical survey of medical psychiatry, remarks upon the fateful view and organicist emphasis in Kraepelin which fore-shadowed Kretschmer's far-reaching hypotheses and in-sisted upon an inevitable course of illness within two basic psychotic entities, dementia praecox and the manic- depres-sive psychosis. It was not until Adolf Meyer applied the broad anthropological interests of his teacher in early folk, and social psychology that the patient was looked at from the standpoint of his emotional and ideological back-ground; or, as Brill says in his *Lectures on Psychoanalytic Psy-chiatry* from a "normal psychological viewpoint." Brill goes on to remark of Meyer's tutelage:[39] "We were taught to describe the patient's attitude and manner, his anthro-pological make-up; we examined all phases of his orienta-tion, memory, judgment, insight, etc." This was, of course, in relation to physical and neurological examination. It was at Bleuler's clinic at Burghölzli, in the company of such anthropologically-inclined figures as Jung, Brill and Riklin that the early association-test experiments of the 1900's were developed under the direction of Bleuler and Jung. There the word, "complex," originated to denote a past, repressed (and complex) emotional experience, and new descriptions of illness varied the earlier essentially dual and rigid nomenclature, the schizoid and syntonic categories of a later Kretschmer classification.

But even before American psychiatry became interpreta-tive rather than descriptive under the combined influence of men like Adolf Meyer and George H. Kirby, or even through the influences of Bleuler and Brill, an unintended by-product of Kraepelin's organicist and descriptive interests had taken him, following his Dorpat professorship, on a tour of various countries. His travels led to keen observations that his major psychopathological categories, and the sub-types within them, varied with culture. While widespread, they occurred in somewhat different arrangement and frequency in different cultures. In Java, for example, melancholia and mania were rare to begin with, and a clinical variant was the absence of any notion of having sinned as part of a depressive reaction. There were, further, no cases involving alcoholism among Javanese, and this category, as "alcoholic psychosis" in Kraepelin's system, showed elsewhere considerable cultural variability. His dementia praecox typology, on the other hand, was not only of frequent occurrence in Java but resembled the presenting symptoms described on the basis of European experience.

Ziehen's notations of differences in incidence and specific symptomatology in Holland and Thuringia; Bleuler's on English, Irish, Bavarians and Saxons; C. G. Seligman's paper on New Guinea in 1929[40] emphasizing confusional states rather than systematized insanities and disclaiming any cases of manic-depressive disorder in acculturated areas of Papua; and J. Dhunjibhoy's in 1930 [41] on regional aspects of India, already alluded to, represent the early pioneering to the third decade of the century roughly, in the field of cultural variation in symptomatology.

For the period from 1870 on, but preceding Kraepelin's discovery that the echolalia, echopraxia, "automatic obedience," and loss of will,—all characteristic of the Latah illness of Malays,—were indeed important elements in the presenting symptoms of schizophrenia of certain types among Europeans, the tendency to note crude variations by region or culture gathered momentum. Kraepelin first published on this disorder in 1896. *Dementia Praecox* was again published, in the Edinburgh edition, in 1919. For the period before, Edward Stainbrook has summarized the extensions of horizons in cultural psychiatry very well.[42] In those years, he notes, it was possible to read in the psychiatric literature frequent assertions that illness incidence, poverty and population density were connected phenomena. Following the economic depression of 1875, it was claimed that an excessive rate "of melancholy" was admitted to asylums of England and Wales. In Japan, it was reported, possibly with point if not with cultural explanation, that mental illness was more prevalent among the married than those unmarried. Melancholia and attempted suicide was less common among natives of British Guinea than in England.

In Parisian institutions, a British visitor could remark a difference from English asylums in that French children were more talkative and demonstrative, whereas in the American, the patients were noisier and more disorderly than in British psychiatric hospitals. With Bleuler, but much earlier, one observer stated, "No one of experience can escape the impression that the composition and behavior of asylum populations differ a good deal in different parts of Germany." Meanwhile, the impressionistic literature reported the increase in the number of all persons requiring care and of suicides in industrialized countries, the disproportion of suicides being one female to every three males; along with this, one reads of such variations in diagnosis as 5 per cent more "melancholics than maniacs" in Norway, but 24 per cent more "maniacs than melancholics" admitted in England in the same period, or the nonexistence of French hysteria in England.

From 1870 on, according to Stainbrook, an increasing number of observations were recorded on the ecological and cultural "determinants of behavior disorders." By the time H. G. Van Loon in 1928[43] was announcing that the much studied Malays whose characteristic symptomatology in running amok was probably the announcement of dementia praecox in a form typical for them of "aggressive confusion" through long habituation to "hostile tribes" and "jungle villages" and headhunts of "any potential enemy," the scenes were well set both within descriptive and interpretative psychiatry, and in more impressionistic reporting as well, for the anthropological and psychiatric discoveries which were to follow. While acculturation was just beginning to be discussed in social science, Van Loon could define the Latah reaction of Malay women in terms like Kraepelin's, "the automatic obedience . . . principally in those who have worked with Europeans," the imitation and suggestibility assumed to be engendered by contact with those "advanced."

It is the last three decades which have seen regional and cultural variants emerge more clearly. Between these scattered and early references on cultural groups and several modern full-length and volume size accounts of psychoanalytic therapy in a person of distinctive cultural background, there lies a literature now as impressive certainly as that of early epidemiological, and not culturally backgrounded, psychiatry. For the full-length analyses of the last decade, one might refer to two which are popularly known. The most recent, at this writing, is George Devereux's *Reality and Dream*, the psychotherapy of a Plains Indian, [44] and it followed by four years W. Sachs' *Black Hamlet*, an analysis of a South African Bantu. [45]

In the United States, this interest in culturally backgrounded psychiatry did not exactly lie dormant until the third decade of the Twentieth Century. The expanding cultural horizons of anthropology and its importation, as a discipline from Europe, through such diverse figures as Morgan, Brinton and Boas, was matched in psychiatry by influences traceable to Freud and Bleuler, Ernest Southard and Adolf Meyer. Karl Menninger has recently summarized certain trends in psychiatric thought which mark progress in this direction through emphases on diagnostic and symptomatological variability, the treatment of ambulatory and community populations, the influence of cultural environment, and readjustments in theoretical research perspective.[46]

While Adolf Meyer, perhaps more than anyone else, at first gave currency to the descriptive classifications of Kraepelin in this country and these categories of diagnosis received enthusiastic reception in institutional psychiatry, he soon moved from more exclusively neuropathological work into increasing interest in "clinical psychiatry and began to deplore the Pandora's Box of Kraepelin name-calling and therapeutic nihilism." As new proposals for more systematic therapy in severe illnesses took form (Weir Mitchell's rest and isolation methods reminiscent of the later Morita-therapy in Japan might be cited), simplifications of psychiatric terminology, like Southard's in 1918, though based on greater "diagnostic definiteness," did not of themselves ease the therapeutic problem or lead to greater success. Other steps, like Southard's establishment of psychiatric outpatient department operations, Meyer's concept and diagnosis revision, and both his and Bleuler's notice of ranges or groupings of illness rather than fixed entities, opened the way more clearly to the concept of total personality study and advances in treatment based on dynamic ideology rather than static Kraepelinian classification and labels. It was Meyer, who, "influenced by Dewey's pragmatic 'functionalism'," according to Menninger, stressed "the importance of life experiences for the development of a mental illness."

At the same time, the Freudian concepts of personality

function and its assessment were being introduced to America by A. A. Brill, W. A. White and Smith Ely Jelliffe. Their enthusiastic reception, in theory and re-research, if not universally in therapy, was ensured by the support of such leaders as J. J. Putnam, Albert Barrett, A. P. Noyes, Richard Hutchings, Arthur Ruggles and W. A. White. As Menninger puts it, today "the Kraepelinian influence remains chiefly visible in psychiatric case records and in official nomenclature." Speaking of the eclectic position which has evolved in many quarters, he states: "The pseudo-conflict has thus been resolved. Historic vestiges remain; some psychiatrists emphasize adaptation and some adjustment and some repression. Some speak of the total personality and some of character structure. But regardless of how they speak, most psychiatrists now think in terms which express the combined ideology of Freud, Southard and Meyer."

The further step of describing illnesses in terms which include the impact of cultural experience on personality remains to be taken. The principle of homeostasis means little to any psychiatric theory or position if constructive, or destructive, efforts of the organism are viewed as "drives," modifiable by therapy, but not by life exper-ience. If Menninger is right that greater or more pro-longed stresses excite the ego and its regulatory devices to "increasingly energetic and expensive activity in the inter-ests of homeostatic maintenance," how much more is this the case if dominant themes in a cultural system present the individual, typically, with the same stressful situations. The kinds of emergency and regulatory devices which come into play "to control dangerous impulses," or to "prevent or retard the disintegrative process which threat-ens" may themselves be typically called forth *less* by some mystical *deus ex machina* of ego functioning *than* by notions, emotionally founded, of ideal behavior, cultural values, improper behavior, and the actual impediments to happiness, and positive homeostatic functioning, of actual human beings.

This notion is then to be translated into theory directly: what is important, now that clusters of illness and diagnostic prototypes are well established, is attention to the varying symptomatology, the cultural coloring, the actual experiential background of the case. It was to this point that cross-cultural work of the last three decades was addressed. A look at more recent literature on culture and psychopathology discloses that incidence studies and explorations of psychodynamics in various cultures have only just begun.

Let us look at one of the most recent of such studies, Stainbrook's on characteristics of the psychopathology of schizophrenias among Bahians of South America, based on work at the Juliano Moreira Hospital[47] About 80 per cent of these patients were rural Bahians of Brazil, approximately 85 per cent lower class and 15 per cent middle class. Many were from three ecological areas intensively studied by anthropologists. The Bahians, as Donald Pierson and others have observed, are multi-racial and their classes are not closed caste groups although largely identified with color. While culturally and biologically a gradual process of fusion has taken place, the lower and lower middle class hospital population was predominantly colored or mulatto, in large part illiterate, and exhibiting behavioral patterns, especially in religion, of both African and Brazilian origin.

This case is particularly instructive in that it shows relationship between a fused or acculturated social and cultural pattern and psychopathology directly, or between notions of ideal behavior, emotionally founded in cultural values and real cultural contexts, and resulting symptomatology. While of the 200 patients studied, all were diagnosed as schizophrenias, a scrutiny of hospital records, additional and occasionally serial interviews, and partici- pant observation in the hospital life-space, plus projective testing, indicated several distinctive patterns.   In the first place, the psychological distance between psychiatrist and patient, based on class, sub-cultural and hospital role differences, was striking.   After the acute admission phase of illness subsided, the lower class patient generally related to the physician by almost uniformly passive-submissive attitudes.   (The obedience and automatic imitation syn- dromes noticed in other native acculturating communities are parallel.)   As in the schizophrenic behavior of most East Indian patients, overt impulsive and aggressive be- havior was very little in evidence toward any official hos- pital personnel.

Beyond this, women patients much more commonly could verbalize their aggressive and fantasy feelings than men; this verbally impulsive behavior did not carry across, even in the most acutely disturbed women, to sexual acting out since they unfailingly retained their ingrained modesty in dress and posture even when squatting in the habitual Bahian sitting position.   More open ideation and feeling by female patients related *both* to consistent variations in child-rearing differences and the severity of disciplines learn- ed in connection with satisfying sexual and aggressive needs.

However, these patterns in training and expression re- lated equally to the generalized cultural patterns of action for male and female behavior.   As Stainbrook explains, "Bahian psychiatry nonetheless is prone to place a diag- nosis of manic-depressive psychosis, manic phase, on such behavior because of the 'affective' characteristics."   The resulting male-female ratio in manic-depressive disorder is 1 to 4 in Bahian epidemiology and since the lower class patient depressive-reactions are "extraordinarily rare, these figures apply almost entirely to the diagnosis of manic excitement." On the other hand, Stainbrook's restudy of these cases indicates them to be schizophrenias with characteristic affective features. Among the hospitalized lower-class patients, in a 10 year period, no suicidal attempts have been observed. Over half the cases of schizophrenia randomly selected (all under 40 years of age) suffered the loss of one or both parents by the time of admission at an average age of 24 years. Despite the high mortality rates of the general population, such a high proportion of parent-bereaved individuals in the hospital population was striking. It was again associated with aspects of Bahian family structure whereby the mother's near kin resided in the same house or nearby thus increasing the possibilities of substitute mothering and the presence of several, possibly confusing, parental figures. The change in the meaning of parental loss from the experience in the relatively isolated conjugal American family is clear, and it argues that deprivations, substitutions and discontinuities of this order may not be statistically considered apart from the total contours of social organization in ethnic groups.

Further, while avoidance and withdrawal behavior was a steady accompaniment of the life-long difficulties exhibited by these patients in the maintenance of poor object relationships, such catatonic symptoms as mutism, stupor and negativism were unusually rare and almost without exception "the schizophrenic patients entered readily into at least a momentarily responsive and meaningful relationship." In both chronic and acute symptomatology there occurred much less anxiety referable to other persons "than in similar disorders in our own culture." While Stainbrook agrees this observation is admittedly difficult to document with great validity, he illustrates for example the acutely catatonic girl who, with some food retained in her mouth, dilated pupils, great motor inhibition and other neurophysiological indices of extreme fear, nevertheless asserted her fear was of the spirits: "I am not afraid of people because they are human beings."

Other cases of catatonia in which such displaced and magnified fears inhibit motility but allow human relationships of a sort to continue have been reported for the Navajo; and the author in his experiences with Eskimo patients at the Morningside Hospital and Clinic in Portland, a federal center for Alaskan natives, found no dearth of Eskimo catatonics with severe motor inhibitions who would chat amiably and gaily until they focussed on supernatural fears. Obviously, catatonia operates differently if it emanates from different cultural backgrounds.

As Stainbrook puts it, the predominantly lower-class rural patient suffers from anxieties, threats and fears of retribution "interpreted as arising from the cultural deities, either . . . African or Catholic. So, too, for most of the lower class men and the majority of both lower and middle-class women, the delusional restitutional symptoms, either megalomanic or persecutory, were fantasied in terms of the cultural religious institutions. Middle-class men, however, much more frequently 'secularized' their restitutive narcissistic and self-esteem delusions in terms of economic and class conceptions of power," their paranoid ideation more frequently involving threat and persecution felt to arise from other men. Certainly here the difference in psychopathology between the lower and middle-class males relates to the point made, that in Bahian culture the intense mobility striving and identifications of middle with upper classes do not affect the lower-class Bahian. Nor will it involve the female (of lower class) whose involvement in religious behavior is as much greater as her economic aspirations lessen.

Equally striking was the fact that paranoid conceptions of impersonal causation (electricity, physical "waves," etc.) were found only in the relatively educated middle-

class, private psychiatric hospital-patients of the Sanatorio
de Bahia where the greater impersonality of aspiration and
economic strivings were maintained in the normative cultural pattern. It is possible that an inverse proportion
existed as between women in *Candomblé* cult organization
and those who succumbed to idiosyncratic, autistic features.
Those in sufficient control of autistic and impulsive behavior were able to conform to the relatively rigid, ritualistic
group activity and passed from the period of probationary
scrutiny into the possession dances. This "psychopathological screening" which distinguishes highly individualized hysterical dissociative behavior from the induced and
nonindivualized conversion phenomena of the ceremonies
argues against the common assumption that normative
ceremonial behavior, such as Hindu-Balinese trance-dance
states may be read off as "cultural psychopathology." The
assumption of Benedict, Mead and others of a total relativity of culture and the abnormal, of cultural-clinical
types, is a confusion of culture with cultural stress system
and with incidence data. As Stainbrook described the
content of *Candomblé* behavior, it was accompanied by
considerable psychopathological screening. As a normative pattern, it "played a significant role in the thought and
action of the schizophrenic lower-class patient," sometimes
characterized by non-institutional meaningless "acting out
of being possessed by an African god of goddess." However, a correlative observation "concerns the apparently
low incidence of gross hysterical dissociative reactions
among the lower-class Negroes in Bahia." This includes
women who in *Candomblé* organization could not induce the
socially approved conversion behavior, but who in personality characteristics were anxious, stubborn and hostile, no
doubt others for whom the conversion phenomena acted
as a cultural "safety valve," and still others who passed the
organizational screening with flying colors.

The distinction between clinical and cultural manifestations is so brilliantly clear in Stainbrook's discussion that it resolves in a major dichotomy: "The clinical picture was definitely schizophrenic and not simply hysterical and usually occurred as a reaction to a situationally acute stress or deprivation. The major psychological goal achieved in the psychotic resolution seemed to be an identification with the omnipotent deity similar to the brief and transitory introjection and identification achieved" by the religious participants during the end processes of possession and conversion.[48] In brief, clinic is not culture, but cultural phenomena greatly affect the etiology and symptoms of psychopathology. The hysterical features in Balinese dances are probably not "schizoid."

A frequent distinction between the epidemiological and clinical approaches is that the first method is by definition extensive and the second intensive, the larger studies filled with inescapable errors, the smaller richly studied and accurate. It is stated above in respect to etiology and the question of cultural background, that all studies, epidemiological or clinical, must have necessary etiological reference or they cease to be psychiatry at all. The limited number of illness groupings, like the schizophrenias, and their almost universal extent in the reported cross-cultural literature suggest universal compensatory and repressive psychic mechanisms or defenses, at human disposal, but with different frequency and amount (or intensity) in given cultural contexts. Three limiting factors in addition to pan-human psychic processes can therefore operate: the cultural context and certain subcultural features such as socio-economic status; the specific conditions of a life course as these become operative in the particular psychodynamics of an individual case; and the stress system inherent in a culture under certain conditions of time, place and circumstance.

Before Stainbrook, in acculturated Bahian society of Brazil, made his remarkable studies of variations from Anglo-American and European forms of catatonia, C. Lopez reporting in the German literature in 1932 noted that no schizophrenias whatsoever could be found among Indians of interior Brazil although acculturated tribesmen living in coastal towns and settlements evidenced the illness in one or another form.[48]   Such variations, from high to practically null incidence roughly correlative with cultural differentiation within a nation of "nations," argues for a range of psychodynamic processes and tendencies in the historically changeable modes of mental illness in Brazil. Further, the swift shifting in a generation of central tendencies in respect to the promotion of a kind of illness in each cultural milieu argues against an indiscriminate use of general terminology of the Kraepelinian sort.

When Ellsworth Faris, in the *Nature of Human Nature*, reported on culture and personality differences among the forest Bantu of Africa, his account was based on four hospitals of the more urbanized areas in which not a single case of schizophrenia or manic depressive psychosis was found.   A subsequent search for the characteristic symptomatology of these illnesses in the outlying native villages of the region fared no better, the Bantu-speaking villagers being mystified by descriptions of the Western disorders. On the other hand, as is well known, the physiologist W. B. Cannon has analyzed the data on deaths due to extreme fears, wasting away and physiological dehydration stemming from a series of cultures in which the religious ideology concerning witchcraft attacks or the breaking of taboo systems may cause fundamental and lethal disturbances of autonomic functioning.[49]   While "voodoo" death and voodoo erotic patterns are psychosomatic disturbances rare in Western European cultures, it must be remembered that they occur within values systems in which the pervasiveness of religious belief in the total round of economic and social life is very great. Such nonliterate peoples have no Sundays and it is impossible to extricate magical belief from the continuity of life processes.

Variations in circulatory and respiratory behavior run parallel, John Gillin's account of magical fright (*espanto*), with its "jumpiness" of pulse rate in San Carlos being just such an instance.[50] Jules Henry has reviewed the psychosomatic literature from the point of view of cultural variability and finds in one instance which he has studied first hand, the Pilagá Indians of Brazil, that somatic disorders center in areas of speech, hearing and muscle function; the same study indicates that the common psychosomatic ailments of Western cultures are completely absent.[51]

Anyone acquainted with the enormous anthropological literature on conversion hysterias and psychosomatic disorders among nonliterate peoples cannot fail to be impressed by the frequency of such directly somatized symptoms in these cultures as contrasted with the totally disorganizing illnesses of our own. Ebaugh notes that the frankly expressive (histrionic, in our culture) type of individual, with inner needs to obtain approval, attention or rapport, tends to develop the somatic manifestations of hysterias, as in paralysis, spasms, anesthesias and pains, or disturbances of such partially voluntary autonomic functions as eating, vomiting, breathing, coughing or lower bowel control. These correspond to the common ailments the shaman cures. Persons showing marked obsessional trends, including such ritualistic rules as temper control, cleanliness, punctiliousness, emotional constriction, and sado-masochistic standards of dutiful or truthful behavior tend to develop the often deeper seated vegetative neuroses and organic psychosomatic disorders. While the primitive literature, by and large, is full of the former, and our own of the latter dysfunctions, particularly in recent times, certain more specific rate variabilities are regularly found in the Western European and American literature. Ulcer of psychosomatic origin has been described as a middle class disease, but the duodenal ulcer variety and childhood asthma occur more often in males than in females. Worthy of note is the shift in sex ratio of peptic ulcer from being predominantly a female disorder in our own culture to one characteristically a disease of adult males.

While more than one psychosomatic disorder tends to appear in the same patient, no large study has been made of the fact that they occur usually at different times in the life cycle. While commonly also, the same disorder occurred in parents, relatives or siblings, such patterns of somatic identification have not been studied in any charted kinship sense nor have the comparative age studies been made in this sense despite the phasic nature of many of these ailments with their periods of crudescence, remission and recurrence. Such considerations require research on somatization of cultural strains. Exophthalmic goiter, gall bladder disease and rheumatoid arthritis afflict more females than males. Certain illnesses which occurred more often on the distaff side (as, peptic ulcer, exophthalmic goiter and perhaps essential hypertension) in the Nineteenth Century, have since appeared in increasing proportion among males during the Twentieth. Other diseases, like diabetes, which were predominantly male diseases of the last century have conversely increased among females of the present time. The fact of higher rates for the latter among both sexes and especially the males of Jewish and Italian cultural antecedents argues for studies in this area which combine sex, age and cultural criteria and which are historically oriented.

As Ebaugh states, "The phenomena of 'sex shift' probably provides a statistical indication of the changes that have taken place in the 'personality type of the sexes' as a

result of social changes that have led to 'female emancipation'." We should add that this is less a matter of blurring
of sex differences in social participation, the feminizing of
males and masculinizing of females, as he suggested, but
differences gradually developed in the social role of each
in the cultures from which they stem.[52] Such studies
should be culture-specific. The related phenomena of an
age-shift, the fact that certain of these illnesses are increasingly appearing in younger age groups (most noticeable in
one large study of gastritis, peptic ulcer and anxiety states)
is evidence that the social position of the sexes, more likely
than biological difference, underlies these trends. The
increasing incidence of psychosomatic afflictions on a non-
hysteriform level in the modern world argues that the
emotional lives of masses of adults, in Ebaugh's terms,
"have become increasingly disturbed, diverted, frustrated
or distorted." Increasing frustration of creativity, the
need to achieve safety or security by obsessional mechanisms, the aimlessness, decline of firm life goals and values,
and the standardization and mass production extending
to information, entertainment, clothing and education are
some of the factors in social environment alluded to as
possibly important.

Two recent investigations into the problem of management of angina pectoris in geriatrics cases conclude that the
prevention of unpleasant emotional contacts will greatly
reduce the gravity and frequency of anginal attacks. The
study of the personality type and psychotherapy in patients
with hypertension, pseudocyesis, pancreatic disease, Men-
iere's disease, and various dermatoses have, in separate
monographs, recently been concluded. Portis, in his latest
work on *Diseases of the Digestive System* marshalls a lengthy
chapter and 70 selected references on the subject of emotional factors in gastrointestinal upsets. It is possible that
both the deeply rooted somatizations as well as the most

incapacitating disorganizing illnesses are more prevalent in modern societies than in nonliterate cultures.

While no doubt the major functional psychoses occur in all cultures and psychosomatic symptoms involving virtually all somatic systems can be found throughout, there are notable differences in symptomatology and incidence recorded to date within various cultures. E. Winston, in attacking the extreme Rousseauan theory of a total absence of any mental disease among primitive groups, early aggregated the material from Margaret Mead's *Coming of Age in Samoa* (Appendix IV), extrapolated from the sample of cases cited, a mere six in all, and arrived at an incidence rate of 100 psychotics per 100,000! The fact that *Coming of Age . . .* patently describes a highly acculturated fringe of Samoa, despite popular assumptions to the contrary, and that figures derived from intensive anthropological observations in community settings are not comparable with those for admitted patients to public hospital facilities destroys this comparison based on a few cases.[53] A recent extrapolation from nine Saipanese cases, giving the astounding rate of 208 cases per 100,000, cannot be justified any better as incidence data though the psychiatric materials by A. Joseph and V. F. Murray in their volume, *Chamarros and Carolinians of Saipan: Personality Studies*, are clearly superior.[54] Most studies, ever since Vilhjalmur Stefansson's comparison of the unacculturated Greenland Eskimos with good mental health statistics, and the acculturated Alaskan Eskimos with decidedly poor rates, have distinguished carefully between the acculturated communities and those which are relatively untouched. While the Rorschach records obtained from frank psychotics among Saipanese show the same disintegrative patterns and serious decrease or loss of reality testing as do the records of psychotics in our own culture, it is debatable whether such a test of personality structure and psychodynamics offers the same opportunity as the Thematic Apperception to draw out differences in content and psychological experience. It is even a question in highly acculturated situations whether reality testing and disintegration are distinctions fine enough to do more than separate the very well from the clearly ill regardless of cultural context or the sub-types of disease groupings.

On the more solid grounds of symptomatology, there can be no doubt that psychopathology is culturally influenced. Geza Róheim in 1939 and P. M. Yap, in 1951, have published over a decade apart on the rapidly expanding literature of this type.[55] More pinpointed and richly descriptive studies like Stainbrook's among Bahians, E. S. Carpenter's among Aivilik Eskimos,[56] and the Berndts among Australians in West Arnhem territory[57] have since appeared along with one account, partly historical, by A. N. Berenberg and A. Jacobson on Japanese psychiatry and psychotherapy.[58] Both Carpenter and the Berndts document cases of psychoses in highly primitive cultures, technologically speaking, though neither adduce epidemiological incidence data. In each study, nevertheless, religious values and conceptions are ingredient in the etiology of the disorders, fear of witches being as important in Aivilik psychotic distortions as mistaken identifications with "the omnipotent diety" were in Stainbrook's Bahian cases. While the Japanese material is more concerned with Morita's methods of therapy in application to psychoneurotic character disorders and obsessive-phobic states, the reliance there in therapy of followers of Morita's Zikei University group in psychiatry upon culturally acceptable principles of Zen Buddhism merely strengthens the contention that religious values may configure prominently in the psychic economy, both as regards the illness and its treatment. In a more general sense of cultural influence, Jules Henry has suggested that the cultural milieu creates at once "the conditions for its own pathology (schizophrenia, for example) and its treatment (introspection and highly developed verbalization)."

In Western countries, the incidence of various kinds of mental and psychosomatic disorder has fluctuated or changed remarkably in populations where there is no evidence for connected changes in race, somatype or genetic composition. The contemporary rarity of "the French hysteria" anywhere in Europe; the increase in instances of peptic ulcer (in the Mauve Decade in New York, 1880-1890, and for a decade following, there were seven female to six male cases of perforated peptic ulcer, whereas in the Depression Period of 1932-1939, the ratio had changed dramatically to twelve males for every female case of tissue perforation);[59] or the fact that in World War I hysterical blindness and paralyses frequently afflicted American soldiers, while in World War II they suffered more from psychosomatic disorders of the digestive tract,[60] each constitutes a variation explainable only by a psychosocial analysis.

E. H. Ackerknecht has gathered comparable materials for similar short periods of time on a variety of nonliterate cultures such as the Kirghiz and finds that where reliably reported, shifts in psychopathology can be equally sudden and sweeping in the primitive scene.[61] Rate variability, in these instances, already suggests that processes of culture change and acculturation operate on psychodynamic levels as well as the cultural, and are as modifiable on the one as on the other. The idea of Adolf Meyer, that within such a generalized disease grouping as the schizophrenias, themselves containing similarities as well as differences, modifications can occur by reason of environmental factors, is suggested by rate variability in a number of other emotional illness groupings.

For those who maintain precarious contact with reality

or those who break seriously with real goal orientation, no clear picture is as yet afforded as to *what* overloading of what emotional or somatic circuits causes a particular disturbance. It is clear however, that interpersonal and human relations contexts, best called cultural, determine not merely whether fissures will occur in personality structure (a problem of indicating incidence), but more particularly in what area of personality adjustment they will appear, which is in final analysis a question of typology. The therapeutic predicament in psychiatry, one of dealing with end-products or epiphenomena of longstanding disease processes, and even more so the special danger of breaking through the psychic defenses of persons who have built them with frenetic purpose, poses problems in the analysis of schizophrenias for typological research results.

A continuance and expansion of Meyer's work requires moving beyond such designations, already over-generalized, as "the schizophrenias" to sub-varieties which relate lifelong situation-contexts to resulting personality contours. One course which has been suggested to overcome diagnostic pigeonholes is to study the longitudinal life course from infancy on out, a method which has been partly realized in studies limited to childhood by René Spitz in the United States and John Bowlby in English maternal-deprivation cases. Ordinarily, for a longer life process, such methods are costly and the shot is scattered; they are appropriate in the children's institutional settings in which they have been attempted. Follow-up studies, in remission states, are also decidedly useful since they have been made with persons whose ego functioning and innermost problems are to some extent known.

Far better, for cross-cultural analysis, is to study sociocultural factors in etiology directly, using cultural push therapy and positive cultural identifications to build upon strengths and avoid weaknesses in the precarious structure of a problematic personality. This method has been dimly apprehended in part in occupational and recreational therapy, but still utilizes all too little what meanings and attachments men have lived by in their best, and most maturing, periods. Such studies, if made in institutional settings, must build their own data beyond the existing record. Examples of religious variability which may be missed by social over-generalizations (as serious as the over-generalized schizophrenias) are "Catholic," without noting the variance among Irish, Polish or Italian Catholics, "Jewish," without distinguishing German and East European Jewish, or by jumbling under "Czechoslovakian," the patriarchial and formerly rural Catholic Slovakian family, and the more egalitarian or matriarchal, often urbanized and virtually nullifidian Bohemian Czech. The exploration of existing relationships in both the best human exemplifications of a cultural pattern and in its most dismal failures is the kind of data needed to throw the situational contexts and cultural stress systems into relief. When, on the other hand, researchers have no control over the amount or accuracy of data in record form, or study truncated samples of larger populations undifferentiated as to age or jumbled as to status, the lack of research design will limit the possibility of determining sub-varieties of generalized disease processes and their situational and cultural concomitants.

The limited number of disease groupings, and their presence cross-culturally though varying in rate and typology, suggest universal psychic mechanisms at human disposal varying in their frequency and intensity of use in different cultural scenes. The historically changeable modes of mental illness as these shift within one cultural tradition, in incidence or in type, we have called *rate variability*. However, if culture is not a mere tissue of externals, but is, as it appears to be in any living instance, an ingredient of personality, then as Parsons states, a culture must be conceived as being both institutionalized in systems of social activity and as internalized in individual but statistically groupable personality systems.[62] The recent, unprofitable controversies over whether cultures are entities heavily determining the activities of individual participants, or activities resolving into those of culture carriers, if brought down to concrete data, would soon accord statistical validity to a combined position. Certainly so long as non-idiosyncratic determinants are concerned, they must, in the nature of cases be cultural, whereas the actual lives and emotional contexts of behavior, or ego-involvements, are again in some proposed situations partly personal and partly cultural. The very meanings of normative, or characteristic, or typical, for the term cultural, determine at once that the probable proportion of cultural to idiosyncratic as among individuals will be heavily weighted with the cultural (perhaps nine to one in American subcultures, if epidemiological data are correct). At the same time, within discrete individuals, all we may say is that nine out of ten will show heavy normative and typical trends in emotional balance.

For the 10 percent of mental and behavioral deviancy, we may quote Felix and Bowers. The notion of studying culture and personality in actual, living relationships by any and all field and observational methods which locate the quality and type of emotion imbedded in the social process was founded in anthropology in the 1930's. It has since become congenial in social psychiatry and mental hygiene. The expression, the utilization, and the resultant course of the emotional life, as lived within cultural or subcultural boundaries, now has the kind of documentation which shifts psychiatry from limited diagnostic preoccupations to an awareness of cultural influence. As Felix and

Bowers put it in *Mental Hygiene and Socio-Environmental Factors:* [63]

" . . . The evidence for the cultural determination of ideational patterns and special motor patterns has, of course, long been established. No one can read the cross-cultural evidence without considerable respect for man's ingenuity in creating thought and motor patterns and for the resiliency of the organism in acquiring them and operating through them. The evidence for the group management of emotional or temperamental patterns is more recent, but already many of our supposed facts have been seriously questioned . . .

"Further evidence has pointed to the widespread presence of certain personality configurations in certain societies or societal sub-groups . . . Moreover, within the same society, patterned differences have been described for various status components, including such special categories as oldest as compared to younger sons. In all such cases the personality configuration has appeared to be consistent with the pattern of institutions through which the people lived. This has led to a consideration of the possible existence of a basic character or personality structure in each society with variations for class and other status differentials, a field in which several anthropologists and psychiatrists are now working.

"Evidence at the same time has been similarly accumulating on the relation between the societal setting and personality disorientation. Early and compelling examples of this are to be found in the impact of Western culture on primitive societies, where the proscribing or decay of key elements of the native culture led to a general demoralization, despondency, declining industriousness, increased infertility, compulsive clinging to elements of the traditional culture, etc. . . . Demoralization is not the only direction that behavior patterns have taken under such circumstances . . . and the differential resiliency of cultures to change has been noted . . ."

To assume, however, that such processes as acculturation, or such forces as demoralization are single causal elements of massive proportion in disease incidence is a fallacy of reduction. The lack of certain vitamins in pellagra and beriberi, or the presence of definite agents in lead or barbiturate poisoning are different from disease processes like cardiac and psychoneurotic decompensation in which a complex of factors may play a role in varying combination. The same appears generally true of all psychiatric disorders, that various combinations and admixtures of emotionalized reactions are end-products of internalized or interpreted event sequences. There is, further, no advance warrant that any combination of such factors in any community or culture is an exact duplicate of any other. Nor are they unchanging (the meaning of culture change and of acculturation) so that a dead level of fixity and constancy may not be assumed without anthropological field work before and during case-finding procedures. The fact, for example, that a psychosomatic illness like diabetes was predominantly a male disease during the last century, and has occurred increasingly among females in the present is the beginning not the end of research into cultural etiology. In a useful paper on *Family Structure and the Transmission of Neurotic Behavior*, Jules Henry has provided an interesting coding and tabular system for recording interactions and attitudes, as for example intergeneration harmony and conflict. All these can be dated and developed in time and comparisons of interpersonal family systems to the nth family may be used to quantify. What makes the paper correct in emphasis is the statement that the "cultural milieu defines the limits within which certain types of family interaction can take place."[64] The idea of direct transmission of neuroses from one generation to the next is obviously to be modified by the range of diversities known to exist among intergeneration levels.

There are cultural diversities, or sub-cultural milieus, that exist on generation levels, and which often incorporate the religious difference, the geographic migrant, or those who have experienced social mobility upwards or downwards. Even so, in the latter instances, it is important to settle in each individual situation whether such different factors as mobility aspirations, or parental conflicts and adolescent rebellions, reactivated and acted out, underlie the difficulty. The emotional balances of psychoneurotic and psychosomatic illnesses, clustering in family lines, among collateral relatives, and between married pairs are far from transmissable contagion; but complementary diseases exist from the psychiatric analysis of them, often revealing the emotional balances that have been struck in family structures. Within the individual, too, the phasic recurrence, or progressive substitution of one process for another may indicate either a continuance of a particular inability to cope with stress or a change in pattern. That unfinished business in the psychic economy is not rare is indicated by a recent survey of Bell telephone operatives in New York where recurrence of psychoneurotic absenteeism regularly accounted for the same 25 per cent of the labor force, and appeared in them in high correlation with organic disorders. Corroborative is the research of Buell and associates in Minneapolis-St. Paul to the effect that approximately 25 per cent of the population regularly use 80 per cent of the available health resources.

In European and most American mental health studies, the field research process of obtaining the real texture of social and cultural backgrounds of patients has been omitted, or where included by hopeful intent, it is bound to the rock and limited by the last census tract information of federal origin with no attempt to refine the texture and quality of social living since that date. Where families and cultural communities have dwelled in an area for years and over generations, the absence of a history of the area, qualitative anthropological field work, or census work-ups over time to discern trends are inexcusable omissions.

In analysis, finally, the holding of socio-cultural variables constant to test one of their number should not be confused, by facile explanation, with their presumptively single-factor weight. Any explanation of mass diseases of this sort is not to be sought, as Gordon and associates warn, "in isolated factors, nor in series of factors each operating independently, but rather in a combination of mutually interacting variables that together form a causal system."[65] We may even add probable causal system, for neither psychiatry nor the social sciences enter the statistical scene of epidemiology with pristine innocence of either mental or cultural phenomena. Were this not so, the several multidisciplinary teams in operation could bow out in favor of sophomore guidance under statistical rule. In psychological studies, it is probable that emotion and cognition can not be studied apart from learning and motivation, since each set involves the complementary one. In socio-cultural studies relating to psychiatry, the causal and relational system does not become simpler.

These strictures are warranted in the light of regular, and in some cases recent publication emphasizing single processes and single factors in the epidemiology of mental illness. In a recent paper on Syracuse, New York, matters of high incidence in certain sections of the city, while not always correlated with low economic status in several census tracts, were found highly consistent with the presence of multiple rather than single-family dwellings.[66] In New Haven, the lower social stratum was said to have twelve times the incidence of schizophrenia as the upper.[67] In the classical study of Faris and Dunham on these matters, the story, as we have seen, was put differently: societies in transition were said to contain "natural areas," or ecological segments of an urban scene, which "favored" the development of certain abnormal traits.[68] As they said:

> " . . . Normal Mentality and behavior develops over a long period of successful interaction between the person and these organized agencies of society. Defects in mentality and behavior may result from serious gaps in any part of of the process."

Yet the processes were never specified in psychiatric terms. While the New Haven study of Hollingshead and Redlich aims at more than allusion to "successful interaction," the "organized agencies of society," and "serious gaps" in the interactive process, it deals only with prevalence, the number of mentally ill persons as of a given stated day, with no consequent separation of incidence and disease duration. Thus the high prevalence rates in certain socio-economic strata may reflect an unmitigated course of illness in some persons plus the number of those becoming ill, or seeking treatment as of a given date.

The Syracuse study, on firmer grounds of first hospital admission rates, and dealing with the relatively firm psychiatric categories of cerebral arteriosclerosis and senile psychosis, notes a high mental hospital admissions rate for these and all other psychoses taken as a group in areas of "high concentrations of multiple family dwellings" and in areas marked "by high percentages of people living alone." The presence of census tracts of low socio-economic status, and low incidence rates of the two psychoses of the elderly "casts some doubt on the correlation between this index (of socio-economic status) and cerebral arteriosclerosis-senile psychosis hospitalization rates," according to Gruenberg. Yet the argument to date could be summed up with Faris and Dunham stating merely that older schizophrenics are no more heavily concentrated in central areas of the city than are younger (despite the general youthfulness of

this category as a whole!), Gerard and Huston finding in
Worcester, Massachusetts, that high rate areas of schizophrenias could be accounted for by the drift into certain
areas of highly mobile, unattached individuals (no doubt
many of them ill before arrival), and Morris S. Schwartz's
substantiation that schizophrenics tend to go lower in the
occupational scale prior to hospitalization.[69]   If the additional evidence of Gerard, Huston and Schwartz is accepted, both the prevalence and gross ecological data of
Faris and Dunham, and the prevalence data of New Haven
are open to serious question.   Further the single factor
explanation of the Syracuse report, based on more careful
incidence analysis, loses much of its mystery. The multiple
dwelling, as a way point to illness, or more accurately, to
hospital admission, is discussed tentatively as connoting
social isolation without physical insulation.   The danger
again, of confusing effects with causes in such long and insidious processes as are involved in cerebral arteriosclerosis,
senile psychosis, or psychoses in general, may be noted in
the downward mobility, ecological-area drift, and occupational downgrading which accompany poor mental
health. A second point, in psychoses of the elderly, is the
inevitable age handicap which must first be culturally and
environmentally assessed as cause before it is measured on
the side of effect.

On the other hand, of these studies, only that of Gruenberg in Syracuse, and Gerard and Huston in Worcester,
have the quality of an incidence study. The findings on
human drift, even those on multiple dwellings, begin to
tell us only where the mentally disordered are concentrated,
a point of considerable importance for those interested in
amelioration and prevention techniques. It is no doubt
a fact, as even Algren's *Man With the Golden Arm* and other
fictional accounts of deterioration and schizophrenia indicate, that slums and transitional zones lack the facilities

and technique to brake deterioration and that preventive measures now current do not sufficiently block such zone aggregation, or send adequate scientific help within. Equally, a prevalence study such as that of New Haven, if not adequate to etiological analysis, nevertheless tells us that a continual lack of detection and treatment, and the tendency to use the term, schizophrenia, more freely in lower class contexts, certainly do not mitigate a serious social problem. Increasingly accurate studies on these fronts will aid in spelling out more clearly, however, the kinds of administrative and preventive measures needed in relation to those developing isolation tendencies, facing age with severe handicaps, or plunging into poorer occupational, status and housing levels.

While diagnostics or treatment will require more information on the course of illness in relation to more psychiatrically pertinent factors, the problem of treatment of cases, as they come, has importance side by side with that of etiological, and more basically preventive, questions and techniques. Nevertheless, studies which have been based on prevalence rates and global ecological survey with only the most generalized, quantified data on the population census, housing, socio-economic status and nationality have distinct limits which do not qualify them as cultural, personality, or etiologically speaking, as psychiatric research.

The description or definition of urban ecological areas is a first step, not a last, in the study of the actual lives of people in modern, urban communities. No doubt, the communities or urban regions must be differentiated and viewed in process. Gross statistical data of urban regions are, further, of critical importance in describing the main contours and *outward* living conditions of such areas. However, Robinson, in a brilliant paper on ecological correlations and the behavior of individuals, has for sound reasons of statistical analysis and the apparent inapprop-

riateness of ecological methods to certain kinds of personality judgments, dismissed the method entirely *as a poor
substitute for individual studies (correlations)*.[70] While his points
on the final uniqueness of an individual's behavior are
correctly taken (as they would be also for the uniqueness
of a given illness process if considered in detail), there is no
doubt, nevertheless, that gross urban data do describe in
rough outline the main contours and conditions under
which a culture, or a sub-culture, and the personalities in
it, continually operate. The ecological approach, none
the less, in order to accomplish this aim, must rid itself of a
static quality not merely in terms of human drift within
its framework, but in terms of substituting processual
analysis (the history of an urban area) for the more static
cross-sectional view used so constantly. Shevky and Williams, focussing on just such processes, have generalized
the most important ones rather than merely delineating
the statistical pattern of a current urban structure; and in
so doing have demonstrated a continual change, marked
over generations, in terms of sex ratio, socio-economic
differentiation, increasing segregation of ethnic groups,
and the like. This method, historical in essence, has greater
application to intergeneration data even though it does
not finally account for each individual personality variance. The point is that the gross data, if analyzed in
process of change over time, succeed in describing the
main contours and *conditions under which* a culture, sub-
culture, or the personalities within it operated in the same
time sequences.

The Chicago school of ecology, of Burgess and his group
was able to point out that the medley, or checkerboard of
residential segregation (cultural, racial, or socio-economic)
patterned into a larger set of concentric zones such as
traditional areas surrounding business districts. The correction of this pattern, by Maurice R. Davie, for other

cities, in terms of transportation arteries and economic
growth patterns of urban areas suggested that the developmental process of urbanism cannot simply be assumed,
nor can the usual rubrics of the urban way of life be taken
as existent within each region.   Despite the alleged secular-
ism of the city, its collapse of religious orientation, religious
movements occur constantly in urban scenes and the larger
faiths have there their most significant organizational
strength.   Despite the claim of individual or family job
mobility within the segregated units, tremendous variations and even typical job and industry attachments may
be discerned within certain cultural groups.   In brief,
while ecological mapping is desirable as a first step in any
description of conditions under which actual people live,
it is only the framework into which the texture of social
integrational forms must fit and in which traditional
family-kin systems, church and social organizations function.

In both the Stirling Project and the Yorkville Study,
carried forward in Nova Scotia and New York respectively,
actual inspection by anthropological field methods has
preceded and guided survey tactics, carrying them beyond
the usual rubrics of housing, income and educational level,
or ethnic and religious labels, into the total texture of
functioning social and cultural forms.   The urbanism
hypotheses of weakened social integration, through voluntary organization rather than traditional forms, or the
platitude of weakened social control over individuals
through replacement of family-kin controls by formal and
distant ones may also be tested.   Ogburn's White House
report on the changing family, a Hoover Commission report of several decades back, suggested strongly that the
affective life of the family under urbanism, though changed,
is not modified in the least by diminishing patterns of
affect and emotional solidarity, but quite the opposite,

that lack of wider integrations forced family affective controls to the fore. Similar qualifications must be placed on terms like social disorganization (where aspects of the urban scene like crime or prostitution actually become highly organized), or ethnic disintegration (where the patterns of politics in city after city proclaim the existence of such formal entities).

In a Czech or Slovak community exemplified in culturally determined formal organizations, and a Hungarian community characteristically lacking in them, the affective backgrounds of social life are not even begun to be studied until family and kinship determinants of affective behavior are known in the normative patterns of such subcultural groups. The notion that, in urbanism, expedient ideas of morality take over where absolute, rigid codes of values leave off may be tested in German-American communities, like Yorkville, where patterns of cultural conservatism operate against resiliency to preserve the standards and values of first generation backgrounds. Beyond this, a pattern of acculturation may, depending on cultural groups and socio-economic contexts, interplay with urban settings in such a way as to affect the rate of change. The pace of acculturation varies notoriously with cultural group and from society to society, affecting upward social mobility and achieving a different degree of stability in different cultural groups. In New York, for example, the rapid pace among Puerto Ricans, which has not yet stabilized, and the notoriously slow pace among Irish point not only to different religious, political and economic values in the two groups, but to size of family-kin groupings, the points in time at which they enter into urban economic life, the stability of family forms, the status valuations, and the conditions within the host culture. The given status aspirations and economic placement of Hungarian-Americans and Puerto Ricans in a given decade may be simply not comparable without taking cultural variations into account. A hypothesis which otherwise failed to consider historical, economic, and social variations in subcultural groups in favor of ecological generalizations on the area as a whole would contain its own assumptive artifacts.

Ecological survey is the first mapped assessment of an area; but it cannot be assumed to touch the cultural and historical conditions under which a group of ethnic variables operate. The same strictures apply to psychiatric evaluations of people in an area which apply to cultural and socio-economic variation. Methods such as the Rorschach, the TAT, the Cornell Medical Index and others will simply not operate uniformly across cultural boundaries. In one study of the Cornell Index in application to a variant culture, the Okinawan, the psychiatrist L. G. Laufer reported, in the *American Journal of Psychiatry* recently, upon its inapplicability. The usefulness of these methods, however, in probing these differences *provided cultural variables are understood* is quite another matter. Similarly, in questionnaire technique, differences by cultural group in initial refusal rates, or in suspiciousness and guardedness, may be more characteristic of Germans, for reasons of cultural standards and values, than in Italians of first and subsequent generation levels. Blocking, fantasy, repression and defensive lying, or oral acting out, boastfulness, impulsivity, and crude imagination may be more characteristic of people in one group than in another. Questions of emotional constriction versus expressivity, the kinds of sexual and parental identifications, or the place of fantasy and imagination in early training are all, as with historical and cultural inquiry, prior to assessments of what is cultural and environmental and what is idiosyncratic in responses.

In much the same sense, Solby, in speaking of group

therapies (like occupational, musical, psychodrama and group psychotherapy) has said that differences in individual backgrounds make these supplementary, not individualized, treatments in which "lack of knowledge of the dynamics of the group as such . . . at present limits the extent of this new therapeutic procedure." To test these emotional voltages, one must obviously know, for example, when suspiciousness is culturally sanctioned in some rural ethnic peasant backgrounds, or when it becomes part of some individually autistic pattern of behavior. In either case, the inducement of emotional response has cultural and social patterning along the way, but in the one case these are externally sanctioned and expressed in the best of reality senses and within "normal limits." In the other, patently, the emotional economy is not really developed in patterns of communication or constriction with others, nor shared with them; but is internally produced, internally compelling, and basically threatening. No wonder then, that the most highly autistic systems are only in small measure and rarely in details culturally predictable, and the more completed in airtight, delusional compartments, the more liable to burst out in strange, noncultural systems. While etiological factors are situated back in time, the losses of realistic ego-directing capacities, of control of impulses, of sexual identification (and its displacement in autistic systems) are all situational losses in the sense of cultural backgrounds and the normative values and stresses they induce.

The interest in deepening ecological methods to include cultural background and the specifics of psychopathology is primarily in the usefulness of such expanded horizons for generating and testing hypotheses about the etiology of mental disturbance. The *how* and *why* of malfunctioning, or healthy adjustment, both products of culture at its best and at its worst, must be tested not within affectively empty frameworks, but in terms of the values, standards and actual lives of actual people. Epidemiological research, again, may be used to express the ratios of every category of illness incidence to healthy populations, but at some point it must turn away from preoccupation with amount to the study of actual cases within ecological *and* cultural frameworks. The idea of utilizing a questionnaired sample for the drawing of cases of normal and aberrant for further study, can, for any area, be linked with the study of psychopathology and cultural background directly in hospitalized cases. Such findings, if applied later in preventive programs or in action settings (hospitals and community clinics) have the practical value of essentially therapeutic and etiological work in British social psychiatry under the influence of John Bowlby, Maxwell Jones,[71] Aubrey Lewis[72] and others. In American programs, few studies have left their communities better than they found them, and few demonstration areas of this sort have been linked with epidemiological research. While the work of R. A. Spitz,[73] for example, has been parallel to that of John Bowlby,[74] the exigencies of the British postwar scene have forced more practicality into the latter program.

Equally important in the sense of larger populations and etiologically pressing problems are the attempts to specify particular psychopathological differences in American cultural groups. The well-known higher incidence of alcoholism in the Irish has been noted by R. F. Bales,[75] only two years later than claims of a greater incidence of sociopathic disorder in Italians of the Boston area were remarked upon in studies of Hyde and associates of Selective Service registrants.[76] Even the different rates of suicide in western countries, or in Ceylon or Japan[77] can clearly be related to cultural, or specifically religious variations, high rates in Czechoslovakia, Germany and Switzerland being matched by low rates among the Irish (Eire and North Ireland), Ceylonese or Dutch. Writing of clinical work in the Northside Center for Child Development in New York City, Drs. Stella Chess, Kenneth B. Clark, and Alexander Thomas have discussed the importance of cultural evaluation in psychiatric diagnosis and treatment from the point of view of noting variations in cases which would otherwise be confusing.[78]

Speaking of both the British and American experience in culture and personality studies, Aubrey Lewis has this to say:[79]

"Individuals are the objects of a psychiatrist's daily concern; consequently he cannot help looking at the problem of interaction between individual and culture from the individual's standpoint. This point of view has its most extreme statement in psychoanalytic theory, which makes the individual incorporate his environment rather than interact with it. As Ernest Jones put it, human behavior is not the product of interaction between the external world and the inner urges and cravings of the individual, but 'it would appear to be nearer to the truth to describe it as the interaction of two separate sets of internal forces on the outer world . . .' He is, in short, concerned almost entirely with what man does to, and with, his environment, not with what it does to him. With this extreme position goes, of course, a corresponding emphasis on the relations between individuals, especially within the family, transcending the influence of the whole social heritage, i.e., the culture. Not every psychiatrist accepts the psychoanalytic view of this—even psychoanalysts, for example Karen Horney, desert it. . . . Consequently in studies that originate with the psychiatrist there is a strong bias. The psychiatrist moreover is so close to the problems of his patients (which are disclosed within the same culture, usually, as that the doctor lives in) that he forgets that some of these problems might cease to be problems if the culture changed . . ."

As E. M. Lemert states in his *Social Pathology*,[80] there is first of all the difficulty of quantitative and qualitative studies in mental disorders where the amount and particular varieties of the illnesses, or even their presence or absence can in certain instances become a matter of dispute, even among psychiatrists. Lewis goes on:

> " . . . We are apt to say that this uncertainty of detection and diagnosis is an overrated difficulty in psychiatry, but it seems to me that it is a fundamental weakness in any studies that profess to be exact, and that it, quite as much as the number of independent uncontrolled variables, makes the study of large groups with the appropriate statistical treatment essential, rather than the minute studies of individuals which have hitherto been the psychiatrist's more usual contribution. To come back to Lemert's work. He considers the ethnic, economic and cultural characteristics of those admitted to mental hospitals, taking these characteristics as indicators of role, status and cultural conflict. He looks at the situation in which the mental disorder developed; the social context of the illness. Then he takes in turn a number of socio-personal matters: the common beliefs about mental illness . . ., the institutions developed to meet the real and supposed needs of the mentally sick person and of society in relation to him, the changing attitudes in different classes and in different cultures and countries at different periods, . . . the social structure of the mental hospital . . ."

While Lewis lists the different problems associated with age and sex arrangements in various cultures, it is obvious that throughout both he and Lemert have been speaking broadly of cultures, classes and the importance of environmental contexts. To this one might add the recent work of Stanton, Schwartz and Davies at Chestnut Lodge where aspects of psychopathology seemed to be a response to therapeutic milieu.[81] That the latter can itself be viewed as a cultural setting, of a sort, is seen in such phenomena as further withdrawals conditioned by lack of understood communication, or by soiling which vanishes in more proper environments, where lack of authoritarianism and higher social expectations in the hospital setting respectively lessen the intensity of defiant behavior.

These viewpoints place a particular obligation upon the science of psychiatry at this time, which has, moreover, much to do with individual therapeutic perspectives over and beyond the importance of environment in general disease etiology. This obligation has nowhere been put more simply and cogently than by Redlich and Bingham in their book, *The Inside Story: Psychiatry and Everyday Life.* Here the authors feel one should know about cultural backgrounds of patients consistently so that psychiatrists in actual practice can judge which of their patient's "odd seeming thoughts, feelings and actions are the result" of cultural teachings and which come from his own "unique development." According to them, it is essential that the doctor who wants to "help us relearn" should understand the cultural background and learning milieu in which behavioral reactions were formed. [82] If *stress* is what is happening in the interpersonal relations of a patient's particular case, we may be sure it is produced not merely in terms of energy and its psychobiological processes of transformation, but in terms of linked cultural and personal realities in which coded symbols as mediating agents mark the quality and quantity of these very relationships.

Neither qualitative nor quantitative assertions about hostility, fear, anxiety, displacement, or repression have much meaning without reference to the analysis of how energies are typically used or dissipated in a culture, a family, or a person. On the other hand, personality traits may be qualitatively and quantitatively discussed with far more meaning for the individual when the thoughts, feelings and actions that summarize his behavior are seen in relation to the thoughts, feelings and actions he experienced in his total life course and his total cultural milieu. The contrary theory, that symbols are merely coded signals of human energies and their processes of transformation, begs the questions: To whom and from whom? And for what socially realistic or unrealistic purposes?

Diethelm has recently summarized the same points;[83] under the heading of *Changing Psychopathology*, he wrote:

> "Psychopathology, i. e., the science of abnormal mental functions, studies the individual patient's behavior. Much stress has been put on certain symptoms which were assumed to be of fundamental importance and theories frequently developed from their occurrence. With environmental changes, including therapeutic and cultural influences, some of these symptoms have become less frequent, others varied their character, while a third group has become more obvious. It is of scientific interest to study these changes and important for treatment to determine how the frequency of psychopathological symptoms can be decreased.
>
> "Hysterical reactions present a well-known example. In medieval times and until the eighteenth century, these symptoms frequently related to religious aspects and to witchcraft. In the nineteenth century, hysterical convulsions seemed of utmost importance to the physicians. All these symptoms are now rarely seen and phobias, varied physical symptoms which correspond to current illnesses, and sexual difficulties have taken their place. A considerable number of psychosomatic disorders may belong in this group."

Diethelm describes several changes in the characteristic symptomatology of the schizophrenias. Catatonic posturing, including catalepsy, prolonged stupor and other evidences of autistic withdrawal; smearing, echolalia, echopraxia, neologisms, and manneristic activity; and symbolic destructiveness are all rare in modern psychiatric hospitals. The once common involutional melancholia of a decade ago, with "the classic symptoms such as agitation, distorted hypochondriacal delusions, or delusions of excessive sinning are infrequent . . ." He continues:

". . . The acting out of a neurotic and psychopathic nature and the uncontrolled behavior which led to loss of human dignity is less marked. The factors affecting this change may be related . . . above all to cultural attitudes. . . .

"In psychoneurotic illnesses, the obsessions, compulsions, and hysterical symptoms have decreased in frequency while anxiety symptoms, phobias, and psychosomatic symptoms are prevalent. Depressions of psychoneurotic origin seem to be more common than at the beginning of this century. In manic-depressive illnesses psychologic and definite psychoneurotic factors are increasingly recognizable and have affected the treatment."

He concludes that contemporary cultural investigations are required for obtaining a clarification of the "meaning of the changes in psychopathology."

While W. S. Robinson, in his paper on *Ecological Correlations and the Behavior of Individuals*, has argued that a set of ecological correlations tends to overestimate the relation among variables since these same variables can also be more carefully assessed in direct relationship to the individuals concerned, the same claim can scarcely be aimed at the meaningful cultural background of an individual as internalized and interpreted in life experience. In this sense, A. R. Martin, in earlier descriptions of Yorkville cultural communities, described the "emotional climate of the home" for each cultural group not as a fixed quantity of precise mathematical definition, and found everywhere, but as a central tendency or generalized matrix of family relationships, activities and dominant values systems, no two instances of which were presumptively identical.   In anthropology even earlier, Edward Sapir in his work, *The Unconscious Patterning of Behavior in Society*,[84] though insistent upon the uniqueness of a given life experience, nevertheless noted the same generically operative tendencies so far as the realm of essentially cultural behavior was concerned.   In the expansion of his work to the interrelationships of culture and psychiatry, Sapir still said of the system of *necessary* connections, "A personality is carved out by the subtle interactions of those systems of ideas characteristic of a culture as a whole, as well as those systems of ideas which get established for the individual through more special types of participation with the physical and psychological needs of the individual organism."   It was these last that Sapir called the "individual sub-cultures."   The implication of a second *necessary* connection between culture and mental illness was stated as in inevitable relation between personal meanings and cultural symbolisms:

> "The personal meaning of the symbolisms of an individual's sub-culture are constantly being reaffirmed by society, or at least he likes to think they are.   When they obviously cease to be, he loses his orientation.   A system of sorts remains and causes his alienation from an impossible world."

The necessity for psychiatry systematically to gather data on both normative social and cultural backgrounds in contemporary cultures, and to consider these last in terms of the systems of meanings which always configure in the foreground or background of individualized cases, is a function of known and inevitable relationships between culture, personality and mental illness.   Humans are unconscious of the grammar of the languages they speak, of the symmetry or formal regularity of kinship systems, though it is there, of regularities in etiquette and custom, though they exist, or of central tendencies in behavioral processes referable as Florence Kluckhohn has termed them, to cultural orientations.[85]

Just as some etiological studies summarize personal and cultural data in their inevitable relationship, so any departure from this principle tends to be etiologically meaningless. The ecological studies which strip down the term, environment, in the context of social psychiatry, to single noncultural factors like nearness to business districts, and the like, ordinarily attempt to argue *post hoc, ergo propter hoc*, and to claim strong etiological significance for these detached items of larger complex variables. We have already alluded to H. Warren Dunham's interesting work on the social personality of catatonics in slum areas. This paper, in 1944, was important in describing the plight of sensitive, self-conscious, schizophrenic individuals in poorer districts, as well as in flagging our attention to the "quiet ones" of such districts.[86] The claim, however, was that the slum area intensified such anxieties in such individuals, and in this sense had special impact on those who became ill. It is questionable, on second glance, whether catatonics are merely so produced; ordinarily, their illness is of a sort where impingement of practically any setting other than the protected hospital environment is often greatly disturbing. There is no study of the relative incidence of childhood schizophrenias from this and other sections of a city and no studies of particular, early developmental problems associated with such settings. While it is possible that the person with timidity and sensitivity responds poorly in this most unprotected of environments, it seems equally likely that parental overprotection and solicitude, plus worry and rejection over mishaps, may contribute more to the original response of self-conscious timidity than the grosser characteristics of the slum environment. From the clinical point of view, the factors having direct and character-forming influence in early development are more basically etiological, the others merely exacerbating in the light of already established and deeply founded features of personality. The question of where deviancy or psychoses begin is clearly one in which data on the earliest development of psychotic patterns, a problem of incidence, are required.

At this point, it would seem that withdrawal, isolation, deviancy or psychotic patterns, in order to worsen, would first be exacerbated in emotional home climates and in family settings primarily, and only further intensified if at all in the neighborhood and district. Obviously, the cultural viewpoint, as exemplified by meanings and values, attitudes and goals resident in socio-economic status and sociocultural, or ethnic, groupings, must be tested before single factor analyses may be taken seriously. This is not to say that the experience of social isolation, or narcissistic hostility, or anxious and dependent emotions do not fit into the development of schizophrenia. How they do, or how they are engendered in family, in socioeconomic and in cultural matrices is the real question.

As John A. Clausen and Melvin L. Kohn have recently pointed out:[87]

"It is now generally recognized that ecological processes tend to sort out not only sub-communities but also sub-cultures . . ."

Selecting ethnic group membership and social class as most relevant in determining the indices for a cultural frame of reference, they continue:

"Studies of the personality development of children from the lowest levels of the status system of American society have indicated several intense value conflicts to which they are typically subjected, especially from the time they enter the middle-class-oriented school. The instability of the expectations developed by such children (and the deprecatory self-conceptions built up through internalizing the judgments of others) likewise may be expected to lead to the development of personalities which are highly vulnerable to stress."

They add that, "Though the difficulties peculiar to lower-class status are most striking, it should not be forgotten that the middle and upper classes produce their own varieties of stress." This view of social class as a species of subculture in the American scene has considerable importance provided ethnic variables are considered along with social status differentials. As they say: ". . . Ecological studies can serve as a stepping stone, but . . . too often they have left the investigator stranded in the middle of the stream." That social stratification in part governs "what happens therapeutically to a person who becomes a psychiatric patient" was recently demonstrated in a study by Leslie Schaffer and Jerome K. Myers.[88]

Talcott Parsons has not only discussed medicine as a part of the social system, but like Leo Simmons and Harold G. Wolff has investigated the social roles of professions concerned with illness as well as the attitudes towards illness which appear in social structures. Since mental illness is as much, if not more, a type of participation in, and reaction to, social processes, as it is "an entity" residing in a person, such studies as these which describe and analyze the therapeutic milieu in terms of realities of social structures throw light upon the total environment into which the individual is born and in which he grows and lives. Franz Alexander and Thomas Szasz, in elaborating on psychosomatic medicine, have included both the biological concepts of medicine, and psychosocial concepts in explaining such illnesses.[89] Even earlier, Alexander added to the usual factors like infant care and childhood experience, the "emotional climate of family," the later "emotional experiences in intimate personal and occupational relations,'' specific personality traits, and relations with parents and siblings.[90] The work of Jurgen Ruesch, done in collaboration with the anthropologist, Martin B. Loeb, at Langley-Porter Clinic, noted statistical series supporting the theory that delayed recovery and psychosomatic diseases together affected more middle class people and those upwardly mobile, as contrasted with conduct disorders ''affecting primarily'' lower class members or those downwardly mobile.[91] Caudill, Redlich and associates have similarly studied social structural and interaction processes on a psychiatric ward.[92]

The point that behavior is patterned, and has cultural or structural contexts, is not novel in anthropology. That the latter concepts of social causality are increasingly used in psychiatry seems also evident. The tendency of psychiatrists, in clinical research or theory, to discount such essentially circular explanations of behavior as ''habit,'' or such fateful ones as climate, race or geography, is partly due no doubt to the constant and healthy contact with changing and dynamic human problems and the steady flow of successes in therapy which argue against too much fixity and rigid determinism in human affairs. Possibly because of these skills and successes, less attention has been paid to the non-biological factors which limit systems of behavior and selectively structure it in one direction or another. Devereux, in noting that these delimiting factors must be of special interest to psychiatry, while not wholly discounting habit in the relation of biological needs and experience, adds a third axis of behavior, the cultural, as one ''which organizes behavior'' through ''the subjective experience of culture.''[93] It must be remembered, however, that both the objective reality of culture and its subjective impact on the individual in actuality organize experience and even human needs as they are commonly met, so that no reduction of culture to biological need satisfaction, as was essentially the theory of Malinowski or to raw experience as was the view of Dewey, really suffices. As Devereux states the case for psychoanalytic anthropology, "Culture is primarily a system of defenses and is, therefore, related chiefly to the ego-functions." It is, provided economics is viewed as being more than just a "nutritional institution," law as more than just a "safety institution," or marriage as more than just a "sexual institution," though clearly all have biological (and *id*) connections. The necessity of recognizing cultural factors as setting more general and pervasive limitations on human behavior than biological needs which, in humans, never act alone, or experience which is never without context, is of crucial importance in the understanding of both normative or aberrant behavior patterns. As Devereux wisely notes, "Symptoms are a result of the reorganization of behavior while the individual is in a state of conflict," but they themselves serve further to organize the "totality of behavior." Such frantic and misguided reorganizations of behavior, no matter how inappropriate and distorted they are as attempts to achieve emotional balance, are developed in the same settings which produce states of recognized conflict, normative behavior patterns, and organizations of a healthy, asymptomatic sort. To separate out the factors, cultural, experiential and biological which operate in unison may be proper for purposes of analysis, provided they are weighted accurately as to importance, are tested in actual interconnection, and are not presumed to be resolvable into airtight compartments, or reducible to the most idiosyncratic and least generally delimiting of their number.

While force-energy concepts certainly operate in all biological (and human) phenomena, they are not delimiting factors which alone direct behavior in either a constricting or releasing form. On the other hand, cultural experience may operate to produce qualitative and quantitative behavioral differences cross-culturally, or within a given cultural system may set the preconditions for the accumulation or release of tensions, the creation of balances and imbalances, the depth of conflicts, and the production of reorganizations or maturity and growth in conduct. That the analysis must be made on both cultural and personal levels in the individual case is true; but in the assessments of types of disorder and cultural background, in epidemiology, the range of such analysis beyond the individual case is equally necessary. The relative durability and rigidity of symptoms in an individual who has developed psychopathology make the task easier, no doubt, for behavioral and cultural analysis in single cases; and by extension, studies of psychopathology in cultural groups are not any more or less formidable, perhaps, than would be complete and rounded studies to a similar depth of normative, healthy behavior.

Variations in Culture and Psychopathology

Striking evidence of differences in the psychopathology of cultural groups has been described by psychiatrists working with African materials. These differences amount to variations in the form of major functional psychoses (the schizophrenias and affective disorders) or in the symptomatology of these diseases and their relative incidence as compared with American and European data. Commenting on the inadequacy of Western standards in application to African psychiatry, D. Mackay wrote in 1948:" . . . We in Africa have not got a Normal for our basis, because we have never taken the trouble to study African normality . . . We have so far judged our cases on their departure from a European Normal, if we have judged

them at all.   Or else we have judged them on their departure from a Normal which we do not know . . ."[94]   J. C.
Carothers, in the fullest survey of African mental health
conditions, adds that while some African patients exhibit
patterns of reaction "similar to those included in neurotic
categories in Europe, the diagnostic criteria applicable in
Europe cannot be stretched to include many other patients" suffering from specifically African cultural forms
of psychoneuroses.[95]   Laubscher's account of extremely
low suicide rates in rural Africa (one per 100,000 per annum,
compared with figures for the United Kingdom of 10 per
100,000 in 1950 and over 11 per 100,000 in the United
States in 1948) rounds out the variation for the cultures of
that continent.[96]

In the form and frequency of psychoses, in the overlap
and divergence in certain psychoneuroses from European
types, and in the incidence of suicide in Africa when compared with modern urbanized nations, the data from this
continent vary from Europe and America.   In addition
to Laubscher's major study of South Africa, there are
Carothers' earlier studies in East Africa (Kenya) of 1948
and 1951,[97] and his more current ethnopsychiatric survey
of African materials.   Tooth, in West Africa, has ably
summarized the Gold Coast data.[98]   A closer scrutiny
of these four studies by psychiatrists is instructive of detailed
regional differences in incidence and symptomatology.
Besides these four, Brock and Autret have described one
variant mental illness found in Africa and known generally
as *Kwashiorkor*.[99]

Actually, *Kwashiorkor* is basically a disease of malnutri-
tion.   It was so described by H. C. Trowell and J. N. P.
Davies in the *British Medical Journal* of 1952.   However,
M. Clark, in the *East African Medical Journal* of the year
before, while noting that *Kwashiorkor* appeared most often
between the ages of two and four, emphasizes the peevish

apathy and catatonic-like inertia and dullness of these children which separate them off from other cases of undernourishment and point to crucial changes in the emotional life. As J. N. P. Davies put it, in the *Annual Review of Medicine* (1952) such a child is "too often a whining, apathetic invalid," permanently handicapped in his development.   Trowell and Davies draw attention to the point that Kwashiorkor is described for several cultures of Africa, Asia and America; Davies (1952) describes the relation of "Mehlnährschaden" in Budapest to *Kwashiorkor* in Africa.

Tooth notes that schizophrenia among adult Africans of the Gold Coast does occur in the familiar European patterns of simple, mixed, hebephrenic, catatonic and paranoid and is the chief chronic form of insanity.   However, Tooth adds:

". . . But whereas in Europeans, the distinction between an affective state with schizophrenic features, and a depressive phase in a primarily schizophrenic psychosis, is a common stumbling block in differential diagnosis, in Africans schizophrenia is more liable to be confused with one of the organic psychoses.   Among the bush peoples, a typically schizophrenic picture is most likely to be due to organic illness, while schizophrenia itself appears as an amorphous, endogenous psychosis.   But the schizophrenic psychoses occurring in the urban, literate section of the population show more nearly the same forms as are found in Europeans."

Moreover, Carothers, quoting H. L. Gordon (1936) and M. Minde of the Sterkfontein Mental Hospital in Johannesburg (1953) finds that paranoia, paraphrenia and even paranoid schizophrenia are relatively rare in Africans.[100] On the other hand, he states as common "a type of twilight or confusional state," sometimes a matter of hours or of weeks but always tending to spontaneous recovery within a limited time; these states appear against backgrounds of physical disease, neurosis or psychosis precipitated by a variety of mental and physical traumata. Anxiety of short duration marks the onset of the more acute cases. "It is always related by the patient to bewitchment and he is fully cognizant of the latter's origin and object. Premonitory symptoms of a Ganser syndrome type, with childish and unaccountable behavior, precede the onset of the major episode, as shown by several writers." Carothers' account of these episodes feature a confusional dominance of action by emotion, an uncontrolled state of fear (panic reaction) or of hostility, a final peak of self-directed violence ultimately visited upon others, and reality distortion with or without hallucination. Recovery follows though a Ganser syndrome or various hysterical symptoms may be left. The entire episode may end with amnesia, once and for all, with apparent normalcy restored and no repetition "unless the cause of the trouble continues in an active form or some new one arises."[101]

Before proceeding with typology in African cultures, it is helpful to consider incidence. Laubscher's 1937 report described a hospitalized population in Queensland of over 550 patients, with some 1700 admissions over a 15 year period. Unfortunately, the descriptions are generalized and not statistically applied to the total 1700. Carothers, as medical officer in charge of Mathari Mental Hospital in Kenya, had opportunity to present admissions data over a five year period concerning 558 patients. He gives an annual rate of 3.4 per 100,000 comparable with Tooth's figure of 3.3 per 100,000 based on the Accra Asylum of the Gold Coast. For Negro-White comparisons in the United States, Malzberg's classic on first admissions to New York State mental hospitals over a three year period remains the definitive work.[102]

In New York, a total annual admissions rate of 150.6 per 100,000 for Negroes and 73.7 for Whites (standardized for age becoming 224.7 and 97.4 respectively) dwarfs the African figures and compares with Carothers' earlier contrast of low figures in Africa and the high annual rate of 161 per 100,000 for American Negroes in Massachusetts. In this period, before antibiotic specifics for syphilis were discovered, the Negro rate of general paresis was 4.1 times higher than the White; that for alcoholic psychoses 3.4 times higher; for cerebral arteriosclerosis 2.9 times; senile psychoses 1.9 times; schizophrenia 2.0 times; and depressive disorders 1.5 times. When allowances are made for urbanization and migration which affect such rates, the differences in rates diminish. For general paresis and alcoholic psychoses in Negroes, Malzberg's finding was that "social factors were largely, even primarily, responsible"; for schizophrenias and depressive disorders, he claimed to find correlations with low economic status, concluding that "the lower economic status of the Negro must contribute directly to his higher rate of mental disease." Only hospital admissions formed the basis of such claims. In connection with his finding that rural Negro rates in America stand intermediate between those of rural Africans on the one hand, and urbanized Negroes and Whites in America, Carothers quotes Wexberg's study of approximately seven thousand Negro and White patients in New Orleans; the major conclusion is that "no evidence could be found of the relevance of biological-racial determinants for the incidence of neuropsychiatric conditions."[103]

Such authors as Carothers, Laubscher, Tooth, or Shelley and Watson were attached to mental hospitals in which circumstances affecting admission are not comparable to *incidence of illness in a community*. However, both Tooth and Carothers made earnest efforts to collect data on the non-hospitalized through surveys conducted by resident officials.

In addition, Tooth's study of the Gold Coast was based chiefly on rural survey in the manner of the Scandinavian community studies, including personal examination of as many reported cases as were accessible at the time. Approximately two-thirds of all reported cases were so examined. While Carothers cites an incidence rate of 35 per 100,000, Tooth reports 96 per 100,000, 60 per 100,000 being examined in the field or in the institution; this ratio of 60:96 examined is high and the disparity of the two figures is accounted for by insurmountable language barrier, native resistance, migration and the like.

Carothers notes that rapid acculturation in the form of detribalization, immigration to urban centers, and employment away from home results in increasing rates of hospitalization for mental disorders. H. M. Shelley and W. H. Watson, reporting in the *Journal of Mental Science* for 1936, add: "When it is remembered that Europeans do not present a united front in matters concerning the treatment of natives (with) one kind of treatment from missionaries, another from officials and another from those engaged in commerce, it is small wonder that the native sense of values is confused and often completely distorted." In support of the factor of acculturation, as affecting illness, Tooth discovered a higher literacy rate than average among psychotics and a semi-rural survey rate similar to that for New York state hospital admissions alone in the one relatively urbanized district of his area (Western Dagomba with its rate of 156 per 100,000). With exclusions of such urban areas, the ninety-six person rate in West Africa would fall considerably. Carothers, in his ethnopsychiatric survey of all the existing African data, including over one hundred and ninety references, concludes: " . . . There is evidence of a disparity between the total incidence of mental derangement in Africa, on the one hand, and in Western Europe and North America on

the other." The rate in Africa, except where acculturated to Western standards, is always lower, and this despite
conditions of considerable poverty and physical illness.

According to D. K. Henderson and R. D. Gillespie, in
their *Textbook of Psychiatry*, the total incidence of mental
disorders as a whole differs but slightly in the two sexes.
In Africa, however, the hospitalized patients show a large
preponderance of males. No doubt, cultural factors again
must be taken together with admissions policies, modes of
detection and differential uses of the sexes of existing facilities. Yet admissions policy and the detection factor alone
could not account for a rate at Accra in 1950 and in
Nigeria of six males to every female, or the difference in
South Africa (1950) of more than two to one. If the high
male rates were heightened by admissions from men's
labor camps or army barracks, Tooth's rural survey of
the Gold Coast countryside still found a ratio of 1.7 males
to 1 female and Carothers' regional survey was similar.
No doubt the acculturation process, even in rural circumstances, affects the sexes differently. Further, a comparison
of age of admission in Kenya and in the United States
would show 78 per cent of African patients between the
ages of 10 and 40, whereas in the United States only 42
per cent are so admitted.

In regard to specific symptomatology in patients from
areas of Africa, the picture for schizophrenias is most interesting. We have commented above on the rarity of
paranoid forms. Carothers adds that this type occurs
more frequently among those who have received a "European" education or an "equivalent type" of sophistication.
Over 60 per cent of Laubscher's South African patients
were diagnosed as schizophrenic (of 7,782 diagnoses to
January, 1951). Laubscher, in separate clinical discussions of over a hundred of these agrees with Aubin[104] that
auditory and visual hallucinations are rarely systematized

or fixed and have a predominantly changing religious mythological content. Laubscher agrees with Carothers also that the "picture of mental confusion stands out clearly above any other syndrome." He had not found "homosexual masking by means of rationalizations and projections among male native paranoids to reach the same degree of defense complexity as abounds among European paranoids." Further, delusions of being poisoned or being bewitched are the most common. Both Tooth and Carothers (1948) are explicit that persecutory delusions are common, with delusions of grandeur rare. And Carothers (1953) quotes Gallais and Planques: "It is nearly always a question of bewitchment, of ill-wishing, of condemnation to death . . ." Tooth observes that schizophrenia in literate, accultural Africans was found to take forms more similar to those seen in Europeans. Laubscher concludes that schizophrenia is the common psychosis of the rural African and that it occurs despite cultural safety valves; moreover, culture influences mental content in these psychoses. In African cultures, this mental content is determined by "the cultural pattern to which the native belongs." In 1937, Laubscher felt that the structure of a mental disorder was somehow immune from this influence. In 1953, after surveying the literature on schizophrenias in Africa, Carothers answers:[105]

> "The present writer cannot agree with this; the structure too is altered. The lack of integrative elements seen in rural African schizophrenia is something more than 'content' and may well have connotations for prognosis. Other reaction types show even stronger evidence of this . . ."

Tooth, describing the schizophrenias in the Gold Coast area, writes: "Among the 'bush' peoples the delusional content was almost invariably concerned with the ramifications of the fetish system . . . An offense has been com-

mitted either against the nature spirits who then trouble
the offender in the form of dwarfs or fairies, or against the
ancestral hierarchy who appear and influence the sufferer
in person." As with Laubscher's clinical notes on over a
hundred patients, Tooth's material reveals that only the
most literate and urban Africans tend to develop ideas of
influence of the European type, that is, *grandiose* delusions
of identification with Christ or God, or influences involving
electricity, wireless, telepathy or hypnotism. Of these,
Tooth observes, "Schizophrenia in literate Africans was
found to take very similar forms to those seen in Europeans." For the rest, his data like Laubscher's, concern
persons poisoned or bewitched by real individuals, confusional states, marked blunting of affect, loosely organized,
autistic thinking, and bizarre, impulsive acts. Laubscher's
observation that 80 percent of the hospitalized practiced
overt homosexuality with no masking or systematized
defenses, the bulk of these classed as "dull schizophrenics"
accepting a passive role, is interesting in view of Freudian
formulations that systematized paranoid mechanisms arise
chiefly as defenses against homosexuality. Carothers and
Tooth both describe as predominant, categories which, by
conventional standards would be termed simple or catatonic schizophrenias, modified by different cultural background.

In regard to the affective disorders, Carothers' survey is
consistent with H. L. Gordon's paper of the early 1930's:
there is a remarkable absence of such diagnoses, except for
a few of the elated type. However, Carothers feels that the
distinction between depressive disorders and anxiety neuroses, well founded in European psychiatry, has had "far
more questionable value" in the African. On the whole,
the figures are low, but even more interesting, in the accounts of Aubin, Tooth and Carothers, brief states of elation are usually described. Though excited, restless, noisy

and irritable, there is little sustained elation, little tendency to develop grandiose plans, and quite often, in Carothers' account, a tendency to show "schizophrenic features especially bizarrely exaggerated movements and facial expressions." To Tooth's and Carothers' statements of low rates for truly depressive states, Laubscher adds that self-mutilation is extremely rare in this disorder; of the 1700 admissions to Queenstown Mental Hospital, only one case in fifteen years was a depressive involving suicide. Concerning etiology, Tooth writes: "One of the most characteristic elements in the depressions of European psychotics is self-reproach . . . but it is certainly true that self-reproach is rarely met with in the content of African psychotics." The tendency in most African cultures to minimize free-will, guilt, and choice in human affairs, and to shift responsibility more to group than personal levels, or grief from isolated to group ritual surroundings may be among the reasons for this resolute turning away from personal fatalism. On this point, Carothers writes:[106]

> "Self reproach and the delusional systems that arise from this are often regarded as secondary manifestations of a fundamental disorder of affect, but it seems that this affect is not sustained without this element and that psychotic depression in the familiar sense can hardly develop in its absence. In fact, organization seems, in mental as in other provinces, to be the determining factor in persistence."

This feeling that the cultural bases in African behavior are different from the European and affect incidence, symptomatology and structure of disorders is borne out in regular variation of psychoneurotic as well as psychotic cases. Aside from the Bemba of Northern Rhodesia whose customs demand a prompt performance of counter-ritual, low rates of obsessive neuroses are uniformly reported. Laubscher notes that a study of various customs shows a factor of atonement towards ancestors enacted in ritual and sacrifice. Anxiety states, likewise, are frequently an outcome of bewitching and poisoning. Phobias related to witchcraft, and physical symptoms in the forms of cardiac or gastric neuroses, or of impotence, refer to putative threats to one's personal and procreative life. Fears of food poisoning and anorexia nervosa, sometimes fatal, suggest what we might call elements of an acute schizophrenic episode. In addition, Dembovitz in his work with West African troops, noted that hysterical symptoms and conversion mechanisms appear so readily that not only neurotic depressions of the reactive type, but even anxiety states and true psychoses are colored by them. The physical symptoms run the gamut of globus hystericus, aphonia, paraplegia and monoplegias, deafness, blindness, tremors, rigidity, and hyperventilation tetany. The predominant mental symptoms include amnesias, fugues, fits and stupors.

Elements of acute schizophrenic episodes, possibly catatonic, are indicated in twenty-one cases of 609 first admissions diagnosed by Carothers as "frenzied anxiety." Such cases, and others described by Laubscher and by Shelley and Watson resemble the classic Malay *amok*. Laubscher has described "acute hysterical attacks, resembling Charcot's grand hysteria . . . but the picture presented is typical of emotional abreaction and follows a dramatic frustration and thwarting of impulses and desires. Of course, this is attributed to some possessing power; this is more the recognized way of reacting to such disturbances than a spontaneous, unconscious discharge of libido in motor acts without conscious plan or design."

Yet Laubscher, Shelley and Watson, and Aubin all describe high homicide and low suicide rates in connection with such impulsive and furious attacks, Laubscher characteristically translating into such Freudian terms as "less introjection of sadism." Aubin's description of paroxysmal manifestations (motor and psychomotor, sensory and psychosensory, ideational and affective) and the episodic fury and terrifying hallucinations which sometimes accompany them, again suggest transitory phases in a schizophrenic process in which the acting out of emotional impulse is freer than in European models, and the disorganization potential is less. After recovery from these states, or in periods between them, seemingly normal conduct is possible.

Dembovitz writes at length of running amok in West African troops, distinguishing the true berserk who fights to the end from the hysterical form, who hurts no one and is readily subdued. Recurrent confusional states and common hallucinatory experiences are spoken of as occurring in anxiety states which do not necessarily imply a psychotic episode. "Normal Africans see and speak to their dead parents." Different from denial is the "disavowal" (*reniement*) of Aubin, "which excludes from consciousness all situations seen as dangers" whether real or magical and including dangers concerning the group such as the breaking of taboos and customs.

This central core of confused, excited, incoherent and emotionally labile ideation and affect is found in most disorders whether they pass under the European labels of hysteria, anxiety states or schizophrenias. "In short," Tooth concludes, "the cultural environment is such that short-circuit reactions . . . released from the inhibitions of intellect are not only tolerated but encouraged." Perhaps this is too strong. Gallais and Planques note that the intellectual and affective factors are closely interwoven. It remains to point out that these are of a different order, understandable only in the light of a different cultural background.

Carothers' summary for recent African psychiatry is

succinct. In elucidation of the difference, he writes:[107]

> "In general it seems that the rather clear distinction that
> exists in Europeans between the 'conscious' and 'uncon-
> scious' elements of mind does not exist in rural Africans.
> The 'censor's' place is taken by the sorcerer, and 'splits' are
> vertical, not horizontal. Emotion easily dominates the
> entire mind; and, when it does, the grip on the world of
> things is loosened, and frank confusion takes the place of
> misinterpretation. All the neuroses seen in European indi-
> viduals are here, as a rule, resolved on social lines; and the
> structure of psychoses is so altered by the lack of conscious
> integration that these are apt to take amorphous or abortive
> forms."

Perhaps this sort of summary is just the beginning of a
statement of differences, not the end-product. There are
certainly far too few discussions of specific psychopathology
within the boundaries of particular cultures and with
reference to specific degrees of Europeanization or detribalization. Nevertheless, the accounts to date from widely
scattered provinces of Africa, including the Cape, East
Africa and the Gold Coast are remarkably contrasting
with Europe and North America and surprisingly similar
one with another. If we list the differences, they are: the
paucity of paranoid forms and masked homosexuality,
unless Europeanized; the confusional or excited catatonic
phases of schizophrenia; the so-called "frenzied anxiety"
with hysterical elements (Carothers and Aubin); the lack
of truly affective disorders of the depressive type, or of
long-lasting and systematized delusions; the fact that
Tooth stresses the lack of certainty in assigning schizophrenic patients to one European category or another,
and his observation that under "home care they did not
exhibit the clinical variations as clearly as those that were
seen in the asylum"; and finally, the variations in delusional content by culture. These differences all point to

a gross but regular variation in psychopathology. On specific points of agreement in the three regions, as with the relative rarity of affective disorders, statements are exactly comparable, Laubscher stating that depressive forms are rare (6.7 per cent for males, 6 for females and only 3.6 for Queensland Hospital patients), Carothers finding a comparable 3.8 per cent in Kenya for 1939-1943 later rising to 6.1 per cent, an incidence figure similar to Laubscher's. Tooth's field survey of necessity yielded higher figures, diagnosed as "mania" or "hypomania," but some probably are schizophrenics in acute episodes (hear voices, are manneristic, show bizarre ideation). At any rate, Tooth writes of Accra: "The absence of depressed patients is most strikingly demonstrated by a visit to an African mental hospital where, under infinitely more depressing conditions, the atmosphere of tense unhappiness usually found in European mental hospitals is replaced by one of unrestrained and misdirected exhuberance of spirits." In contrast to the African patients at Mathari, Carothers notes elsewhere for this area that of two hundred twenty-two admissions of Europeans, a high of 22 per cent were depressed.

Turning from Africa, analyses of mental hospital admissions for New Zealand and Hawaii have been supplied by the anthropologist, Ernest Beaglehole. In each case, the interest has been in comparison of native groups, Maori or Hawaiian, with migrant populations from Asian, European or American cultures. In his first study, in New Zealand, admissions for a 10-year period, 1925 to 1935, were made for Europeans on the one hand, and Maori or part-Maori on the other. Unfortunately, congenital disorders like mental defectives or those having relatively low intellectual endowment were not distinguished from acquired defects, so that incidence of functional psychoses may be blurred; moreover, Maori culture was decidedly modified by the time of this study, the Maori being an indigenous population long subject to acculturation. When the rates were standardized for age, however, they were 8.37 per 10,000 for Europeans and 4.19 for Maori. These rates applied only to hospitalization, *not incidence* in community settings. As such, however, they are of considerable interest inasmuch as there is no good evidence that by the late 1920's and early 1930's there was this large a difference in attitudes towards hospitalization or accessibility to facilities in the two cultural groups.

Concerning symptomatology, the Maori of New Zealand contrast with the data from various African cultures in having a remarkably high rate of "manic-depressive psychoses" not shared by the Europeans. Maori females showed a rate of 52.6 per cent in this category of all first admissions in a 10 year period. One might suspect variance in "schools" of psychiatry to account for these differences in diagnostic category, but fortunately for the contrast, British psychiatry has dominated both the New Zealand and African scenes. The relative incidence of schizophrenias (not differentiated as to type) was roughly similar for Maori and European. Official Fijian figures for 1936 which are included show a hospitalization figure of only 1.6 per 10,000 for Fijians, 4.05 for Europeans; the differences between New Zealand and Fiji in facilities, modes of detection and community attitudes toward treatment may be reflected in these results. At any rate, for those interested in the problem of the rapidly acculturating alien in an inimical environment, the comparative crude totals for Chinese and East Indians are 530 and 161 per size of population (100 being the proportionate share according to population size.) These figures are not standardized for age and can only tentatively be compared with the corresponding per population figure of 40 for Fijians (1.6 per 10,000) and 96 for Europeans.[108]

Beaglehole's comparative Hawaiian study uses the sample years 1930, 1935 and 1936, employing the same ratio of 100 as being the proportionate share of mental illness according to population size. Here native and part-Hawaiians were distinguished, the former having a ratio of 200 per population, while the latter ranged from about a fourth to a third of this figure. Native Hawaiians had not only twice the expected amount of psychoses, but figures ranged to three times the expected or proportionate amount for Puerto Ricans and five times for the tiny Korean population. A large population in the Islands, like the Japanese, were comparable with the part-Hawaiians (about 75). First admissions figures in this study showed the same comparative rates as prevalence figures. This study centered in acculturation phenomena and both Hawaiians and part-Hawaiians, despite the differences between them in general incidence, showed variations in incidence of particular disorders. Hawaiians had the lowest rates of schizophrenia (30 to 43 per cent); part-Hawaiians an average proportion. Hawaiians had a high proportion of depressives ("manic-phase," in this report); four-fifths were "manic." Part-Hawaiians had the lowest incidence of such affective disorders, with no recorded excess of the "manic" form.

Beaglehole concludes that the incidence of psychoses rises in cultural groups confronted with the necessity of adapting to "Western forms." This is more the case, he holds, for Hawaiians, Puerto Ricans and Koreans. The case is distinctly unclear unless it is meant that the major Japanese migrations were earlier and more sizeable than those affecting Puerto Ricans and Koreans. The Hawaiians, while indigenous, were certainly dwarfed by successive waves of migration to their shores. More interesting, perhaps, is that the acculturation process for part-Hawaiians here decreases the chances for paranoid forms of schizophrenia to arise, and likewise decreases markedly the incidence of affective disorders in the "manic" form. Together with the high rates of hospitalization for the native population, these results contrast surprisingly for the findings from Africa which are diametrically different on each score.

When it is remembered, however, that the "native Hawaiian" represents a minority, not an indigenous majority, and one schooled for decades in American and Euro-Asian cultural practices, the mystery disappears. Far from being a native culture in the beginnings of the acculturation process, it is, as Beaglehole rightly felt, the longest acculturated, problematic minority of the Islands. However, with the Puerto Rican predominantly a Spanish cultural form and the Korean an Asian, "Western patterns of culture" would seem too narrow a term for the several patterns which dominate Hawaii. On the other hand, Puerto Rican, Korean, and more recently Filipino rates of disorder have illustrated more current struggles to adapt, and a faster current pace of acculturation in each case reflected in far greater incidence rates than is the case with the relatively settled populations from Japan, from Okinawa or resulting from part-Hawaiian miscegenation and acculturation.[109]

In North America, Hallowell's study of two groups of Salteaux Indians of the Berens River District was based on field research which disclosed one to be highly acculturated, the other less so. In the acculturated "Lakeside" group, according to intensive Rorschach investigation, 81 per cent of the best adjusted and 75 per cent of the maladjusted had their place of provenience. His conclusion is that under conditions of acculturation, some individuals make "excellent, even superior adjustments; others fail to make as good adjustments as under the old regime . . ." The more restricted range of adjustment, he feels, is consistent with the fewer choices or conflicts of the less acculturated society. While not all persons are prone to feel the destructiveness of such conflicts, their presence in an intrapsychic sense may, according to Hallowell, precipitate disturbance in those susceptible individuals represented in the 75 per cent of maladjustment at Lakeside.[110]

For the same cultural area, both Ruth Landes [111] and J. M. Cooper[112] have reported on the *windigo* psychosis of Ojibwa and Cree Indians of Canada. This disorder combines homicidal behavior with cannibalistic fears and tendencies in a culture where life-long food frustrations and oral sadistic behavior appear to be outstanding features. For the same setting, Hallowell has taken pains to show how language, belief, art and mode of life in a culture are related to perception, "how they become involved in the perceptual experience of individuals, the role they play in the total structuralization of the perceptual field and the consequences of this fact for the actual conduct of the individual." As Hallowell notes:[113]

". . . Entities that have *no* tangible or material existence may become perceptual objects in the actual experience of individuals . . . In the foregoing anecdote there are thirteen references to *hearing* the windigo . . . The sounds heard by A "meant" *windigo* to him. But this was possible only because cannibal monsters were among the traditionally reified concepts and imagery of his culture. Furthermore, just as a word or a sentence may induce an affective response or immediately define a situation as dangerous and thus call forth appropriate conduct, such was the case here. Once the situation became perceptually structuralized in this way, subsequent sounds likewise become meaningful in terms of the same pattern. . . . "

For some time, the manner in which *certain types* of autistic auditory and visual hallucinations arise in psychotics of given cultural background has remained a mystery.

This applies to the stylized hallucinations, auditory and visual, in the African data, in European or American patients (Christ, God, radio, telegraphy), in non-psychotic vision quests of Plains Indians, or here, again, in *windigo* (named for an Ojibwa-speaking monster with cannibalistic tendencies). That a culture can affect visual perception, and concepts about spatial relations in the "tangible or material" world, varying perception in the normal and abnormal dimensions of conduct, was shown by Hallowell elsewhere in his discussion of perception and spatial concepts among the Salteaux. There he wrote:[114]

". . . The level of abstraction utilized in dealing with certain spatial attributes is not a simple function of maturation or intellectual capacity on the part of individuals. It is a function of the status of the cultural heritage as well. For the cultural heritage of a people, among other things, limits or promotes the manner in which and the terms in which the individual deals with the spatial attributes of the world about him. If a culture does not provide the terms and concepts, spatial attributes cannot even be talked about with precision. Individuals are left to fend for themselves, as it were, on the level of elementary discriminatory reactions. This limits the possibilities for the mental manipulation of more refined and developed concepts that require symbolic representation in some form. Without such instruments in the cultural heritage certain areas of action are excluded and the solution of many practical problems impossible."

On the other hand, as comparative studies of art from modern and nonliterature societies will indicate, a cultural pattern will reify not only types of concepts, but forms of imagery even as to intensity, realism, emotional impact, distortion, rhythm, balance. What it *promotes* in types of emotional expression is of equal importance to what it limits, omits, or suppresses. The same observations apply to the auditory and visual ranges of perception.

Thus Joseph and Murray write of Rorschachs of any isolated rural population in a manner which reminds us of the contrast between rural natives and Europeanized subjects in Africa. Discussing the psychological test materials of Chamorros and Carolinians of Saipan, the authors state:[115]

> ". . . A high degree of associative concreteness is to be expected in any people who have not at their disposal the general and abstract associations which are provided by a 'higher education'. We may, for instance, anticipate much concreteness in the Rorschachs of any isolated rural population . . . "

The lack of delusional systematizations in a wide variety of mental disorders of nonliterate peoples: the "running wild" of Fuegian tribes (Cooper, *op. cit.*), the Greenland Eskimo *piblokto* (women running about naked, Cooper, *op.cit.*), the "Arctic hysteria" of Lapps, Eskimos, and northeast Siberian tribes (Cooper and Yap, *op.cit*), and the similar forms of psychosis, Latah of Malays and Imu of the Ainu tribes of Hokkaido (Yap, *op.cit.*, and Aberle),[116] all point to atypical forms of schizophrenias varying from the Western standard. Like the "frenzied anxieties" with hysterical elements of Carothers and Aubin, they remind us of schizo-affective disorders as discussed by Adolf Meyer, but more loosely organized, more episodic, and more bound to action modes of emotional expression than to fantasy. In "Arctic hysteria," Latah, running amok, and Imu, both startle and surprise reactions are common, echolalia and echopraxia predominate, and trances, convulsions, coprolalia, and catathymic outbursts occur. The running amok forms are marked by sudden, furious aggression and hostility visited upon oneself either in the initial or final phases. Erwin H. Ackerknecht early noted similarities in Malay Latah and Siberian "Arctic hysteria" (as reported by Czaplička and others) in which the loss of will and automatic obedience often took forms of echolalia and echopraxia; these symptoms corresponded closely with a type of catatonia once seen commonly in the West but now comparatively rare.[117] Amok, in the Asian, African, and possibly the Fuegian forms refers to violent homicidal aggression with ideas of persecution and possession. While hostility towards a given individual is often in evidence, it radiates indiscriminately and with little delusional systematization towards practically any victims who come to hand. African forms of amok are often self-mutilating initially, the Asian self-destructive ultimately. To the states of homicidal confusion and excitement, *windigo* among the Ojibwa and Cree may be added. Carothers' "frenzied anxiety" certainly belongs to the same list; and H. G. Van Loon's observation, as early as 1928, that dementia praecox "announces itself amongst Malays very often by aggressive confusion" places the classic form of running amok in Malaysia in the same category as that found in North America, South America and Africa.[118]

This category is undoubtedly a variant of Western forms of the schizophrenias, best classified provisionally as schizo-affective disorder. Seligman's "brief maniacal attacks," for the unacculturated natives of New Guinea; similar reports in the incidence figures ("hypomania," and "brief manic phases" of affective disorders) of Africa likewise point in the same direction. The author's experience with epidemiological data in Hawaii in 1949 paralleled Beaglehole's: a stable, large, and long-acculturated population like the Japanese showed few surprises from a Western point of view and generally speaking low incidence, whereas the people most in the throes of initial acculturation, the Filipinos at the bottom of the social scale, showed a high proportion of affective disorders ("manic depressive psychosis") and catatonic confusional states among the Hawaiian hospitalized. In Hell's Half Acre of Honolulu, where immigrant Filipinos undergoing urbanization chiefly dwelled, several classic cases of running amok, and ending in death of onlookers and the aggressor alike, occurred in a brief period of time.

These data, from Asia, Oceania, Africa and the Americas uniformly mark a high incidence of states of confused excitement, with disorganizing amounts of anxiety, fear and hostility present, and frequently associated with either indiscriminate homicidal behavior or self-mutilation, or both, in a setting of catathymic outbursts of activity. The contrast to the West of these nonliterate peoples, Eskimos, Ojibwa, Cree, Fuegians, and various cultures of Asia, Africa, northern Europe, and the Pacific, with their relatively low incidence of depressed and suicidal states suggests that in addition to their marked associative concreteness and high activity and motility orientations, these psychotics more typically direct hostility outward and express it with greater freedom and directness than in European models. That they express it outside of tightly organized family or kinship scenes is also interesting. In European patients, not only will the confusions in sexual identification (homosexual or asexual) be masked by systematized rationalizations, but basic hostility and anxiety will themselves be disguised and internalized with less expressive outlet. In this light, it is entirely conceivable, as Carothers, Seligman and others have documented, that "brief, maniacal attacks," often self-terminating in natural course, are a result of lack of systematized fantasy or delusions acting as ego-defenses and in place of them action and motility functioning. In the West, there are superimposed layers of fantasy.

In a parallel sense, in Western cultures, those emphasizing emotional expression and outlet or placing a high valuation on heterosexual potency, like the South Italian, may be nearer these models of fantasy constriction than those restricting emotional expression by and large, and containing double standards for sexual conduct. In a paper on "Mental Illness in Primitive Societies" by Paul K. Benedict and Irving Jacks, the manuscript emphasizes "the role played by the Judeo-Christian preoccupation with guilt and its consequent channeling of hostility towards rather than away from the self." This is true of the distinction noted earlier by Ruth Benedict in the difference between cultures which emphasize guilt and thus center individual choice and responsibility versus those which control behavior by defining conduct in its context of custom and applying the sanctions of shame to any transgressor. But this distinction of Ruth Benedict in *Chrysanthemum and the Sword*, between what she termed "guilt cultures" and "shame cultures," is only one side of the coin. In psychodynamic terms, we must still know the amount and complication of defenses used against stress, whether rationalizations and delusions are present to constitute a secondary defense system or whether motility and fantasy act together in a more direct sense. In the same way, the psychiatrist must know when, culturally speaking, to expect more associative concreteness to operate in patients, where hostility is turned to self-destructiveness or against others, where the affective life is dulled or made labile, and the roles played by motility and fantasy.

The anthropologist, too, could benefit by knowledge of these distinctions since schizo-affective states of confused excitement have too often in their literature (like Tooth's "mania" and "hypomania") been misdiagnosed as hysterias or as manic states. Joseph and Murray, in their work on Saipanese, stop to note that six Alorese cases in Dubois' *The People of Alor* are diagnosed in error as "manic states" or manic-depressive psychosis. The same authors, in their work on Saipan, are impressed by a higher rate of psychosis among the more acculturated Chamorros in contrast to the native Carolinians. It would be interesting to know whether this is because of deeper seated and long-lasting disorders among the Chamorros in consequence of their greater Europeanization and acculturation.

The work of C. G. Seligman in New Guinea, C. Lopez in Brazil, J. Dhunjibhoy in India, A. I. Hallowell among the Salteaux, and the African specialists, all suggesting higher rates of incidence and greater conformance to Western models in consequence of acculturation no doubt influenced Beaglehole's theories of the late Thirties concerning cultural breakdown and mental disorganization. Actually, five years earlier, George Devereux in 1934, impressed by these world areas materials which were fast accumulating, and perhaps mistakenly emphasizing the rarity of any forms of schizophrenia among them, proposed a "sociological theory" of schizophrenia as resulting when the culture became "complex enough" so that the individual became disoriented as to his social role.[119] Apart from the lower incidence rates of long-lasting disorders, which now seems probable for nonliterate cultures of the world, the present theory of schizo-affective disorders of shorter duration is more consistent with current anthropological knowledge that all cultures are almost equally and infinitely "complex."

The Spencerian notion of Western Europe's greater "complexity," individuality, and personality-heterogeneity; the primitive as custom-ridden, conforming, and evidencing a dead level of uniformity in personal characteristics, is a Western stereotype long since abandoned in anthropological circles. In place of either notions of a Rousseauan lack of worry, or of widespread personality disorganization among nonliterate peoples, or the Spencerian idea of magic-ridden and illogical irrationality among them, it is necessary to note the distinction in cultural types where in one associative concreteness is present, in another lacking. In one scene, more direct expression of emotions is promoted, in another prohibited; in one culture, action and motility in social, economic and artistic life is required; in another ratiocination, fantasy, guardedness and rationalizations abound. As John Dewey stated the matter in *Philosophy and Civilization*, the distance between nonliterate cultures (the so-called "savage mind") and our own Westernized societies is the difference between basically contrasting conditions of existence, modes of life, values and percepts. As he discussed the question methodologically:[120]

> ". . . The tendency to forget the office of distinctions and classifications, and to take them as marking things in themselves is the current fallacy of scientific specialism . . . This attitude which once flourished in physical science now governs theorizing about human nature. Man has been resolved into a definite collection of primary instincts which may be numbered, catalogued and exhaustively described one by one . . . But in fact there are as many specific reactions to differing stimulating conditions as there is time for, and our lists are only classifications for a purpose."

The data on varying normative cultural behavior, and on differential psychopathology in these other cultural scenes demonstrate that the largest unresolvable "differing stimulating conditions" affecting human conduct are cultural in essence. The reach of the cultural factor in any scene, acculturated or not, is undoubtedly great and can affect behavior on normal, neurotic or psychotic levels of expression precisely because of the duration of culture. Its effective stock in trade is massive in proportion to an individual life course and to one's personalized experience and accomplishments. When dealing with the problems of human organic and social life, we must free ourselves from what Whitehead aptly termed the fallacy of "simple location." The human being is never located in a single instant, once cultural forces have taken hold as inevitably they do. In his social and even organic development, the three modes of time, past, present and future, are to be reckoned with as they naturally converge in human thought. Ernst Cassirer, in *An Essay on Man* quotes Leibniz to the same effect: "The present is suffused with the past, and pregnant with the future." Especially where psychodynamic questions are involved in human conduct, the supreme ability of men to bring to bear upon conscious and unconscious motivations the past, present and future, as if these were immediately available, places their mental and emotional functioning in a common setting amenable to the cultural influence of others. In this sense of constant interaction and uninterrupted communication with others on mental and emotional planes, all cultures are equally and infinitely complex. It is this which commends the entire world of culture to our notice for comparative study with attention to specific differences, the specific ideational and emotional conditions of cultural existence.

In *The Future of an Illusion*, Sigmund Freud argues that it would be an advantage to leave absolute values and ideals out of consideration and admit "honestly the purely human origin of all cultural laws and institutions." It would also be helpful to abandon the idea that these cultural values are themselves immutable or rigid in any cultural history. Freud's notion that cultural rules and institutions should serve people, not rule them, or that growth required overcoming fixed conceptions of either rules or institutions is brave advice indeed. "Man cannot remain a child forever; he must venture at last into . . . 'education to reality'," wrote Freud.

However, whether we are dealing with individual super-ego formation, or with the growth and change, under acculturation, in whole cultures, the simple fact is the immediacy of cultural laws and institutions, and their overwhelming importance as a way of life to whole groups of people. There can be no other interpretation to the facts presented that native peoples tend to be hospitalized less frequently than Europeans from the same areas, that the rates rise with cultural dislocations, and that the forms of disorder vary with cultural background. All peoples are cultured, so to speak, and the point is not abandonment of these modes of life which are, essentially, the ways they live. Instead, for psychiatry, there is here afforded a matchless laboratory in which to study the effects of differing organizations and patternings of the life course. This does not mean that valuation, in the sense of scientific and humanistic judgments, is forbidden. Since social psychiatry is concerned not only with the raw data and findings of prevalence and incidence studies, but probes the significance of socio-cultural factors in the etiology and dynamics of mental disorder, it belongs logically to public health and preventive medicine with the need for collaboration with psychology, the life sciences, and social science. It cannot be abandoned to purely personal standards of emancipation, nor is there any indication that it will be.

Psychiatry has scarcely begun to investigate the levels of fantasy and motility usage in different cultures, although Flora L. Bailey[121] and Margot Astrov[122] have reported on the importance of motility, activity and mobility as dominant themes in Navajo literature, economic way of life, linguistic structure, habits and customs. Even earlier, Jane Belo[123] reported on characteristic motor habits of the Balinese, and George Devereux,[124] in 1951, provided a third contrast from the Mohave. For fantasy, there are scattered references, Victor Barnouw's study of the fantasy world of a Chippewa woman,[125] Hallowell's of a dissocial

Indian girl,[126] and Margaret Lantis' and Katherine Spencer's recent accounts of Eskimo and Navajo personality, respectively, as revealed in folklore and myth. J. S. Lincoln,[127] D. M. Spencer,[128] and Dorothy Eggan,[129] among others, have shown that the manifest content, form and interpretation of dreams are largely culturally patterned. Both W. J. Wallace and Devereux have reported on Mohave dreams in much the same sense. Finally, David Efron published a comprehensive study in 1941 on changes in gesture and motility patterns of second-generation American Jewish and Italo-American populations showing a gradual inhibition of motility of the first-generation type, including gestural languages, under conditions of acculturation.[130] The point was not only that specific cultural groups had distinct types of gestural communication carrying qualities of emotional expression, but that these were modified under conditions of cultural change.

Besides acculturation phenomena, wherein new and variant forms of a culture make their initial historical appearance, there is the matter of already existing regional variants of a basic cultural form. For the Italian, and even the acculturated Italo-Americans, Robert Lowie in his *Social Organizations* has applied the term, *campanilismo*, for the narrowly defined solidarity of a rural region and village which may sometimes be extended to town and provincial limits but rarely farther.[131] The existence of these regional differences which are crystallized in economy, custom and traditional history can be traced out, though only roughly at present, in mental health data as well. While Italy's overall commitment laws of 1904 and subsequently, aimed at protection of the general population, and not at patients' needs, Italian admissions rates even in the peak years of the early 1940's ran about 50 per cent lower than the United States. Yet from a regional standpoint, Rome and the area north of it had an annual

rate of 168 per 100,000 hospitalized, while the area south
of Rome plus Sicily and Sardinia had 95 per 100,000 by
the middle of the decade.   Paul Lemkau and Carlo de
Sanctis who have presented these data show care in distinguishing between North Italy, South Italy, and the
islands as to cultural variants affecting the annual hospital admissions rates for mental disorders.

Even the over-all figures for Italy in the Forties which
Lemkau and de Sanctis present (a generalized rate of 59
to 62 per 100,000 population) while it is only a third of
United States rates, or a fourth of Swiss rates for comparable periods, must be considered along with such Italian
customs and attitudes as the care of older, ill persons in
the family household, the blot on family reputation which
may lower a daughter's or son's chances for suitable marriage, and the tendency to equate illness of any variety
with both sexual and personality weakness.[132]   In the
American Journal of Psychiatry for the year preceding the
Lemkau-De Sanctis article, Eric Berne pointed out in his
survey of Oriental mental hospitals that in Ceylon, fully
two-thirds of the patients hospitalized are males![133]   Berne's
further point that Malays do not seem to succumb to
schizophrenias so much as to "toxic confusional psychoses," or the suggestion there and elsewhere that frankly
hysterical symptoms strongly color the illnesses of India
and respond to treatments that incorporate yoga with
modern psychiatric practice are reminiscent of the findings
of Van Loon in Malaysia, Carothers *et al* in Africa on
toxic and confusional states, and Seligman in New Guinea.

The point is that such observations need to be made in
more restricted cultural arenas, where both socio-cultural
backgrounds and policies affecting hospitalization are well
known.   Until this is done, regional cultural variants, and
shifts in illness typology occurring with cultural change,
will not begin to be studied.   The search has led toward

scientific differentiations of types not commonly emphasized in psychiatry as representing its chief traditional distinctions in nosology or diagnosis.   Before proceeding, it will be helpful to attack certain questions in typology directly from the point of view of the kind of social psychiatric theory involved.

"It is a well-founded historical generalization," wrote Whitehead, "that the last thing to be discovered in any science is what the science is really about."[134]   In psychiatry, in the Kraepelinian period of symptom-cluster description, and bounded for the main part by Western and Northern European models of such diseases, the disease process itself, far from being thought psychosocial in essence, was regarded as being founded in biologic and individual psychological event-sequences.   While Adolf Meyer substituted a more functional and environmentalist view of personality as man in action, and Freud and his followers took interest in the family matrix of such activity, wholehearted descriptions and analyses of reaction patterns and formations, according to total contours of the setting and influences which produced them, belong to a later date.   In the brilliant, original work of Freud, for example, the origin of illness in indelible, if often unconscious, memory-traces and in conflicts of *id* and *superego* as individually-centered apparatus pointed back to the start Freud himself had as neuro-anatomist, as an individualist in a setting of then-successful mechanically materialistic philosophies.   The establishment of the significance of dreams, the unconscious, censorship, resistance or infantile sexuality are at best individually-centered concepts.

However much these concepts have reference to family structure in the total Oedipus theory, that family structure is a mechanically-operating invariant, at points similar and at many more distinct from the actual realities and constantly growing data on family structures across the world's surface. Even so, while conflicts of *id* and *superego* go far, as in original Freudian theory, in the explanation of hysterical and obsessive compulsive disorders, the generalization and the restrictive shorthand this theory imposes hardly contain the cross-cultural data. Indeed, it hardly begins to describe the blindness or leg paralysis of two Ute Indian patients, responsive in a matter of days to dream analysis and shamanistic suggestion versus the long-lived and heavily invested hysterical symptoms of an East Indian mystic.[135] They are not the same illness, most often, in the light of genesis, etiology, differences in the setting for growth, and even in reference to the biological and sexual components of their individual features. Even the appropriately called *mechanisms* of defense, for the hysterias, of condensation, displacement, symbolization and secondary elaboration; or for the obsessive compulsive neuroses, of the use of opposites, denial, undoing and repetition, these are circular explanations of symptom entities, or, as Meyer pointed out, not descriptions of *total* personality or reaction patterns.

Identification as a method of learning, again internally descriptive of individual motivations, does not really tell us how those motivations, and not others, first arose. Projection as a method of handling anxiety, stress or frustration is again descriptive shorthand, invaluable to be sure, but known even before Bleuler, and still not adequately defined in terms of the total setting in which it will arise, the ways in which it operates, and the means by which it will cease. While schizophrenias, in Freudian terms, are weaknesses of ego-structure, we are not told, specifically, of what types and how these, too, may arise. Whereas oral and anal, or narcissistic infantilisms are suggestive in some instances, schizophrenias occur in some quarters of the globe in settings of unabated heterosexuality. Throughout the whole Freudian system, culture, human values, and the quality of human relationships in an individual or in a group are epiphenomenal and consequently the descriptive shorthand turns out, all too often, to be not broadly analytical.

In Carl Jung, the test of good intentions fares better for there is definite interest here in the cultural, religious and aesthetic backgrounds of human beings, as well as in the cultural meanings of symbols. Impressed by the presence of opposites, as these occur in fantasies, and especially in the conflictual products of schizophrenic patients, Jung saw in these the archetypes, or images of a "collective nature" sealed in the unconscious of the race. Obviously, the Durkheimian notion of cultural conditioning, of "collective representations," was being used, but now in relation to a new theory of the unconscious, and one having traditional roots. With little anthropology available, free associations were used to discover how individuals failed in reaching life goals. While on the brink of discovering something concerning the differing quality of human relations in different cultural traditions, the delimited area in which Jung worked kept him, despite provocative discoveries from the Freudian quarter and the pervasive influence of Wundt, from breaking with older typologies.

The direct attack on rigidity in typology was reserved for Adolf Meyer, and has been continued by his lineal descendants. Influenced at first by a broader grasp of neuroanatomy and neuropathology, diagnostic terms changed in the direction of reaction types being stressed, with prognoses altered by a somewhat Freudian-genetic and dynamic approach. In therapy, the use of distributive analysis broke the rigidity of the Descriptive School, with the study of the individual and his specific reactions, including his social relationships, taking the place of fixed classifications, or in contradistinction to Freud, in place of the reduction to infancy. With Meyer as with Jung, increasing emphasis on age levels in the life cycle, each age playing its part, and on the cultural and social organization of the family, left but a short step to be taken in defining this part of a science of human relations which could include values and ethics.

Only by a fallacy of simple location do we erroneously regard mental illness as being, on the one hand, biologically ordained, or on the other, individually centered as individual failures. All such disorders, except the narrowing number of those which are overwhelmingly organic in origin, are failures in human relations to be sure, but again, failures which are as attributable to the individual characteristics of the society and culture as they are to the social characteristics of the individual.

Both Karen Horney and Erich Fromm, in separate ways, proposed orientations to psychoanalytic theory which reversed Freud's contention that sexual development determined character, and instead contended that character guides all behavior, including the sexual. Horney, in her discussions of reaction formations in female patients, or in tracing widespread evidences of neuroticism in contemporary American culture, indicates points at which the perpetuation of faulty neurotic solutions to the problems of the feminine role, or the competitive role, occur because of invariant conditions in cultural environment. Fromm, in an even more generalizing vein, has defined and recently redefined social character. In the latest statement, he writes:[136]

"... By 'social character' I refer to the core of the character common to most members of a culture, in contradistinction to the *individual character* in which people belonging to the same culture differ from each other. A society is not something *outside* of the individuals which it is composed of, but it *is* the totality of these many individuals. The emotional forces which are operating in most of its members become powerful forces in the social process, stabilizing, changing, or disrupting it... One has relied much too exclusively on gathering data on what people *think* (or believe that they are supposed to think) instead of studying the emotional forces behind their thinking. While opinion polls are significant for certain purposes, we need to know more; they are not the tool for understanding the forces operating underneath the surface of opinion. Only if we know these forces are we able to predict how the members of a society will react . . . From the standpoint of social dynamics every opinion is worth only as much as the emotional matrix in which it is rooted."

Theories of social character do not supplant those of psychogenesis; they are supplementary to them. Paul Lemkau, Benjamin Pasamanik, and Marcia Cooper, approaching the same question from the standpoint of psychogenetic theory, have reached essentially the same conclusion.[137] Pointing out that psychiatric acceptance of the psychogenic hypothesis implies a "bridge" of causation between prior experience and later illness, the authors add:

". . . This does not, of course mean that we must also accept any particular theory of dynamic mechanism, or even any of the suspiciously direct concepts of personality type such as the oral and anal types . . . It is not necessary to concern ourselves with dynamics according to Freud, Jung, Adler, Meyer, or any other system. All that is needed is to accept as valid the simple statement that life experience not directly affecting the structure of the organism can influence later behavior, and, in extreme cases, lead to symptoms identifiable as psychiatric illness of one sort or another."

Lemkau *et al* note that unless this temporal concept is true, there is no basis for the prevention of basically non-organic mental illness and no hope that mental health can be promoted. If on the other hand, the psychogenetic hypothesis is true, then there logically follow responsibilities for preventive efforts that psychiatry cannot escape, among these the prevention of damaging circumstances or the change in their impact upon personality. The consideration of the Freudian position, in turn, yields the same familiar critique:

> ". . . Freud stimulated interest in the effect of cultural concepts on the individual, but he made few if any suggestions beyond rather vague ones about sex education . . . Indeed, in his *Civilization and Its Discontents*, a product of his matured thinking, he states that civilization can grow only by increasing repressions and consequent neurosis. Freud's major hypothesis is that basically, the human being is ruled by instinct and by innately determined developmental patterns."

Freud said little about prevention of "the disasters he demonstrates so clearly," or, in Fromm's words, he consistently interpreted the dynamic nature of character traits as an expression of their inevitable and often self-destructive libidinous source. The interest of Fromm in a psychiatrically elaborated, and interdisciplinary, science of human relations is paralleled by Lemkau, Pasamanik, and Cooper:

> ". . . Most psychiatrists nowadays either boast of a knowledge of anthropology or apologize that they do not have it. What is such knowledge for? Surely it is not just to contribute to pathology, a dissecting of the threads of an illness to see how it came about. It must also have some value in a more constructive sense, to help explain the process of the construction of the personality as well as to furnish a diagram of its present status. It must be to give hints from comparing different developments in different cultures, so that something may be done to improve personalities in our own land."

In this sense, and in the *American Journal of Psychiatry*, these authors speak of the "eventual prophylactic intent

of anthropological studies." Indications that the even-
tuality is more immediate than appears at first glance are
the astounding number of sub-cultures and cultural enclaves in the United States, the endless stream of ethnic
minorities, the presence of acculturation, culture conflict
and social change phenomena, and the interdisciplinary
interest in the populations of our present day mental
hospitals.

Positive Emphases of the Biosocial Position

The question of whether the psychosocial position is
founded upon, or even proceeds from the basis of any
particular set of psychiatric theories, whether Freudian,
Jungian, Rankian, Meyerian, or any other,—is an idle
query. Today, such a view is open to objection because
it is divisive and limiting. While a biosocial or psychosocial position is more selective than a mere amiable eclec-
ticism, it is not conceived of, or intended as, an exclusive
approach. A scientific method such as this attempts, by
its very nature, to combine certain kinds of data and to
synthesize relevant information.

Consequently, the biosocial position selects from among
behavioral studies of man those which are well-founded in
psychiatric knowledge, and, at the same time, are interdisciplinary in range. Immediately this rules out those
psychological theories which run hopelessly aground on
socio-cultural facts, or which limits their logical combinations and interpretations in theory. With equal force it
eliminates socio-cultural theories which cannot make psychiatric or psychological sense. As a result, the reach of
the psychosocial position, or its applicability, is not intended to promote any tendency to form "schools" in the
form of special, delimiting viewpoints in psychiatry. There
is even less intention to impose single methodologies, or

insist upon predominantly specialized practices of treatment.

In this sense, the position merely serves notice that a body of fact, method, and theory does already exist which is interdisciplinary in character. As method, it may be used among others, or in judicious combination with others. In brief, the force of this theory and method is to view total personality in its total context, the latter connoting psychiatrically relevant aspects of socio-cultural background. Indeed, this last concept is as important and novel today as were conceptions of the importance of the total contours of personality in the time, and the position, of Adolf Meyer.

Any such clearly defined position should announce its own particular methodologic cautions. In the first place, the psychosocial position warns that without this correction in perspectives on mental health, a certain myopia, noted by J. L. Halliday for other fields of medicine, can take hold and set limits to both the techniques of treatment and of prevention. On the other hand, a psychosocial synthesis in psychiatry, while opposed to overly-imaginative or oversimplified organicist emphases, does not simply ride a tide of psychological emphases in the mid-century psychiatry of the United States. Instead, it argues for scientific explorations on every conceivable front, neurological, experimental, physiological and biochemical.

A philosophy of science acknowledges historical and current progress and welcomes continued and balanced maturation in useful fields of inquiry. As is known, no field in medicine can proceed without organicist viewpoints and various kinds of experimentation. More positively, however, it is now known that certain methods of treatment, such as the psychoanalytic, the institutional push-therapies, biophysical and biochemical treatments, or supportive therapy are at one time, or for one patient, entirely appropriate, and at another time in a given course of treatment utterly inapplicable to him.   For another patient, with a different illness, or the same general illness with different prognosis, the same course of treatment may be utterly inappropriate to his needs.   For one, free association may be most destructive; for another, supportive therapy or push therapy may be wide of the mark.   In the light of an enormous array of personality and illness variation, existing on the individual level, the psychosocial methods and insights apply throughout the range of mental disease phenomena, therefore, chiefly in the *planning* of a course of treatment.   In addition, preventive psychiatry has much to utilize here in the improvement of marginal personality functioning, or in the possibility of the prevention of psychological disaster, as Lemkau and his associates envisage it.   Rennie's work on prognosis in the psychoneuroses is, in this sense, a contribution in the realm of preventive medicine, as much as it is a comment on the possibilities of malign and beneficial results of certain kinds of treatment.   The problems of treatment in psychiatry gain in perspective, according to Lemkau, when we begin to relate the hidden needs and status of a case, ordinarily adjudged in the light of psychodynamics, pathology, or personality functioning alone, with those external conditions, past and present, which have influenced individual personality.

At any rate, current methods and theories, founded in single disciplines, are often inadequate to the needs of institutional therapy which must cope with a variety of personalities, and disorders stemming from a variety of cultural contexts.   Such methods are even more inadequate, when used singly, to the still larger task of providing data and practical techniques in the more challenging dimensions of preventive psychiatry.

A single example is apposite.   In our discussions of certain African variations in incidence and psychopathology, we noted the Freudian theory of homosexual masking and paranoid projection and its possible wider application or greater relevance in Western European and American data from contemporary cultures. For the most part, African or even Brazilian or Bahian peoples lacked these symptoms. While such generic groupings as schizophrenias were still common in both settings, paranoid reaction forms were found frequently, in systematized types, only in the Euro-American data. Any reader of the two Kinsey reports, no matter how critical of their sampling and other statistical and conceptual shortcomings, (e.g., the use of orgasm as a unit measure of sexual behavior), will hardly fail to note the amount of homosexual behavior, temporary or sustained, which these reports record for American males and females. Apparently, this is not always latent, much less masked in interview, when it can become a coded and quantified part of a questionnaire method used by Kinsey and associates. If one is aware of the extent of these phenomena, overtly discussed by a large part of this non-randomized and geographically scattered population, subject to interview, he may only guess, in the absence of psychological and personality tests, how much latent or covert, masked homosexuality would exist in a stricter sample or cross-section of American population when studied more intensively.

Consider then, the latent and often covert homosexuality noted in many American psychiatric patients. This is frequently, without correcting for sub-cultural differentials, noticed as associated generally with a wide range of neurotic and psychotic disorders, and has been remarked especially for the schizophrenias showing paranoid reactions. But scientific curiosity, or demonstration and investigation cannot end here. For some time, such anthropologists as Clellan Ford and G. P. Murdock of Yale, working in the field of sexual behavior across cultural boundaries have pointed out that maturation and differentiation of the sexual drive is a matter, very largely, of social and cultural norms and standards. In other related contexts, cultural anthropologists have substantiated a corollary of this first principle and one which goes far beyond a mere Freudian pan-human approach. They have found, in a number of cultures, that children of given sex are virtually reared to identify with parent or with relatives of the same sex, but under such *varying* conditions in child-rearing and cultural practices as quite often produce within a group of children by-products of ambivalence or hate or fear. In some cultures, quite the opposite, the security of love and respect, and positive personal and sexual identifications become a strong central tendency in the psychology of the group. Frequently too, where the psychological valences are negative and destructive of positive identification, the cultural settings as they affect the socially sanctioned, adult sexual models (father; mother; or the mother's brother in a given clan system) are such that these adults are involved in settings, socially speaking, which produce discontinuities or negative emotions in the affective responses of the child.

Such a discontinuity in male identification, for example, was pointed out by Bronislaw Malinowski in one of his many Trobriand Island studies, *Sex and Repression in Savage Society*. Here initial acceptance by a father and positive male-child relationship to him were complicated, in the pubescent period, by the imposition of a mother's brother's authority with its strong overtones of sudden male authoritarian control and rejection. The entire Trobriand myth of the existence of a *Vada* cult, a projection of notions of organized female sorcery, is interesting in the light of this jarring of positive male identifications. So, too, are the "love magic" mechanisms which accompany male trading in inter-island *kula* trade-expeditions, and reported in *Argonauts of the Western Pacific* for males of this same cultural group. In the Trobriands, the same problem is traceable in the cultural notions of a somewhat feminized ideal male type; in the actual sexual practices; in the culturally elaborated denials of physiological paternity; and even in the religious system whereby *baloma* or spirits of the dead impregnate females in their reincarnations by entrance through the woman's head!

Returning to the African materials from certain regions of that continent, the suggestion is tempting that sexual non-identifications and misidentifications are there, by contrast, all the more absent, leaving such problems to Trobrianders or to Americans, chiefly because of differences in kinship structure and social organization which *vary* more in the areas of Africa considered from the model of the classical Oedipus complex. If Malinowski was hoping to speak for nonliterate cultures (in the sense of the title of his book), he chose a poor example, and one which understated his case for differences. He had reason, however, when he protested against pan-human Freudian appraisals. In BaThonga culture, where males also are chiefs and dominate the political and economic sphere, a case of masculine protest against women even more exaggerated than the *Vada* cult is found in their *Beloi* cult. Here too there are serious discontinuities in male identification. Other nonliterate cultures will show, variously, masking, or less overt homosexuality, or even a striking and healthy ignorance and disinterest in homosexual practices.

Our point is simply that research models in the life cycle exist for study in various cultures. All cultures do indeed balance off their statements of the situations bearing on sexual identifications, male or female, with parallel and, at the same time, different models of relationship with parent, siblings or relatives of *opposite* sex. Obviously, the actual balance of relationships to *same* and *opposite* sex operate together. This seeming preoccupation of anthropology with these family and kinship models of relationship, each in every culture with its inevitable guide to duties, obligations and feeling tones, has provided more grist for mills of doctrine on kinship and social organization than for carefully guided studies of the psychological consequences of such systems in which psychiatry and anthropology both participate.

Even though the Freudian system of generally invariant family relationships and dynamics needs to be reviewed and corrected, it appears that Freudian theory has nonetheless opened the door on a most important area of research. The relationship to parent of like sex is important for the individual, especially where conditions promoting identifications, misidentifications, or nonidentifications are culturally structured in easily recognizable form. G. W. Henry's study, *Sex Variants, a Study of Homosexual Patterns*, portrays case after case of such nonidentifications and misidentifications.[138] Even here, in a sample for which cultural background is not discussed or revealed, there are gross differences, for example, between the male *repelled from*, or hostile towards, the masculine role, and one whose emotional interests have been directed exclusively to members of his own sex. One is reminded of Horney's terminology, in another context, of "moving toward," "moving away from," or movement "against" other people, with its connotations, respectively, of warmth, withdrawal, and hostility. Here the misidentification pattern (the one whose interests are directed, in psychosexual behavior, away from those of members of his own sex) may engage in sporadic or active homosexual patterns or have such latent interests. In the two volumes of Henry's study; the first on male, and the second on female variants, the family constellations contributing to such group-ings as he uses (bisexual, homosexual active and passive and narcissism) are unmistakable in deciding the balance, or difference, between those repelled from assuming a mature bio-social role, and who therefore positively identi-fy with the psychosexual role of the opposite sex (mis-identify, in our terminology) and those who are non-identified. There are also those who are confused as to psychosexual role in the sense of being nonidentified, in our terminology. In addition there are some whose identifications and psychosexual affects are merely blurred by lack of any truly satisfying relationships with the oppo-site sex in their prior history (partial identification). No doubt the latter do not suffer the same degree of confusion or distortion as to their basic identity.

In a recent British study of marriage and the family, a research of considerable methodological sophistication, J. H. Robb has presented the same guiding theory, namely, the need to see *how* the family functions as a group, the psychological relations which exist among its members, and the resulting personality balances of its component individuals.[139] Whether one accepts, in whole or in part, a Freudian theory of identifications and misidentifications (or the relation of these misidentifications to hostile para-noid projections), it is already abundantly clear that there is no single model of family organization, cross-culturally, which alone and inevitably operates for the entire human species to bring one type of normalcy or one of sexual aberration to the fore.

Since there is no intention here to confuse clinical cases with normative cultures, let us say simply that a concept of normality always varies with a cultural setting and the conditions under which it functions. It is this setting which determines the normative aspects of social and sexual roles. The range of such variation has, as outer limits which prevent an absolute relativity from operating, certain minimal needs of human beings. These are needs of both a biological and psychosocial nature. In every culture, even the most barren, there are means for obtaining a modicum of recreation, relaxation, and the harnessing of human expressive tendencies whether in art, music, drama, the social uses of leisure, games and sports, mythology, literature and the like. All societies regulate sexual, economic, religious, and social relationships. All contain family systems and classifications of kin as inner limits, while at the same time denoting wider systems of association, which, though having less affective force, particularly in formative years, are by no means always negligible in effects upon the family and the individual. Because of these variations, which are essentially differences in culture, there is no single family model, cross-culturally, bringing one type of normalcy, alone, or one of aberration to the fore. Within a culture, while family types are not absolutely identical, and while individuals differ in sexual, economic, religious and social behavior, there are nevertheless central tendencies in each of these phenomena which make them interdependent, roughly harmonious, and finally a system or type.

On the other hand, a cultural system, by its own inadequacies and "problems" (such as economic uncertainty, war, or kinds of inhumanity or hostility built in it) contains its own historically ordained ineptitudes or incomplete solutions. These problems may allow for the appearance of a range of acceptable social character in most persons, but produce notable aberrations in others. Of importance for social psychiatry is to plot the course, in the phrasing of Lemkau and his associates, for "comparing different developments in different cultures, so that something may be done to improve personalities in our own land." Different cultures contrast in the manner of promoting identi-

fications with adult roles, and their statistical degree of
success or failure points to specific variations in the structure and functioning of family and social group organization.   We add that these particular social structures depend, for their success or failure, not merely upon universal
intrapsychic mechanisms and functions, but upon the culture within which the specific family or group operates.
Obviously, where one finds such symptom clusters as
homosexual trends, aggressive wishes and projected hostility, the combination is intensely threatening to the
patient.   He, least of all, is in a position to assess the cultural factors without assistance.   Yet even how he handles
such trends varies from group to group, as Tooth's and
Laubscher's data from Africa indicate.   The latter component, which is in reality the basic psychodynamics of a
case, depends equally upon the culture, one's experience
in it, and the course of illness.   This is what is meant by a
careful assessment of the cultural factor in each case, and
its contribution in restoring a greater sense of self-esteem,
of kinship and belonging with others.

In discussing nonidentification and depersonalization
trends, or indeed the feelings of unreality which accompany
serious "loss of reality contact," it already appears that
conditions of ambivalent love or hate in parental, or parent-
surrogate roles, may be related to nonidentifications or
misidentifications in the intrapsychic relationships as they
are experienced between a child and parents (or parents,
siblings, peers).   But family systems, or their equivalents,
do not end here.   Family types not only contain within
them the possibilities of this degree of systematization, but
they contain as well a microcosm of all the prevailing
relationships, which parallel or accompany these.   Here it
appears to students of mental hygiene that maternal relationships often are more important, and overshadow the
case, apparently regardless of the sex of child and the total

history of his adult role identifications. But the total balance of relationships with family members have a way of becoming mirrored in other extra-familial relationships. The phrasings, or content of theories about "schizophrenic patients of schizophrenogenic mothers" seems to eliminate the actual balances of relationships with both parents as experienced by a child of given sex and the extensions of relations to others. Bowlby's excellent work on the importance of maternal love in child care has overtones of such one-sided emphasis.

A cross-cultural investigation into family types associated with serious psychopathology must be undertaken to determine, in schizophrenias, where both parents (or their surrogates) are so frequently hated, whether more intensified hostility toward parent of opposite sex is statistically favored. Possibly this is the case in more fundamentally disorganized schizophrenics since greater hatred of the parent of opposite sex is most destructive of latency-period, adolescence-period, and maturity-period opportunities for developing freely spontaneous libidinal or sublimated love relationships. Yet there are other relationships, to work, to recreational groups, and the like. If the theory of degrees of identification were demonstrable, the Freudian theory of the Oedipal conflict as being based inevitably on infantile sexuality and opposite sex attractions would be modified. With parent of same sex the least resented, in serious disorganization, the simple reading of the Oedipal theory would be open to serious question. Actually, psychoneurotics seem to fit this model of greater hostility towards parent of like sex, and to retain not only a degree of identification, but reality contact as well. In the schizophrenias, quite the contrary, the reality contacting agencies of perception, ideation, and emotional evaluation are all strikingly invaded, as a sense of identity becomes blurred or impaired, and as, frequently, body image, sexual identity, and adult social role performance, or even self-esteem, breaks under a battering of hostility sometimes directed outward, but always internalized as well and depressing in its internalized effects.

This formulation is reminiscent not only of the nuclear forms of the schizophrenias, even the short-lived forms of some nonliterate societies; with confusional blocking, acute acting-out of hostilities (external and internal), affective lability and its disorganized lack of control, repetitiveness in acts and speech, and bizarre, uncontrolled compensations against depression; but here also, according to some African materials, frank misidentifications occur as to sexual and adult roles. In modern cultures, by contrast, the schizophrenias seem to fall into this pattern on occasion, but today much more frequently, and particularly in American and Western European hospitals, the illness typology shifts in more pronounced fashion into patterns of sexual non-identification, or denials of misidentification, masked homosexuality, paranoid projection, and more systematized ideational disorders with the sexual confusions so rare in African hospitals so very pronounced in our own. In the light of the greater distance from reality evident in the latter cases, and their longer duration, or lack of spontaneous recoveries (as occur in African "confusional states"), it is hypothesized that greater hatred of parent of like sex often represents cases which show less systematized or florid pathology, even where acutely disordered. Greater spontaneity in recovering reality contact or fewer less intensively used defenses mark this simpler pathology. The more deeply channeled and jarring hostility towards members of the opposite sex may represent a greater measure of degree of misanthropy. What strikes us so frequently in cases productive of the higher degree of schizophrenic isolation, autism, and fantasy is the presence of a more disastrous illness, with paranoid overflow or projection, and its encapsulizing into a private world of one's own making.

Apparently, what W. A. White called "flight into reality" could better be renamed spontaneous recovery or reintegration in the nuclear schizophrenias where actual identity is less sweepingly challenged. On the other hand, the world becomes torturing, distasteful, and a really unreliable framework for existence in the degree to which a realistic self-identification in relation to others of like and opposite sex becomes unbearable. In this light, it is clear why "free association," probing, and the seeking of frank confessions are least applicable to those whose need for defenses is most frantic. The fallacies of hypostatization in Freudian theory may include not only that of an invariant form of family structure, or a single method for analysis of emotional disorder, but also a failure to recognize fully how easily one type of human relationship may color another. Beginnings were brilliantly made with the doctrines of transference and counter-transference. Yet neuroses and psychoses are indeed different in that perception, cognition and the affective life are invaded in the greater emotional disturbance of the latter. So, too, are human relationships more thoroughly disturbed. Even within a category as broad and general as the schizophrenias, cross-cultural perspective suggests a variance in typology based on degree of disturbance, a range in prognosis together with a variety of backgrounds, and qualitatively different forms of psychodynamics referable, it would seem, to different socio-cultural backgrounds.

There are, then, in addition to the usual intricacies of the physician-patient relationship, in some quarters too often delimited to discussions of transference and counter-transference, the further matter of what Sullivan called the "cultural handicaps to the work of the psychiatrist." These are partly resident in the particular quality of the personality and psychopathology of the patient, which a person of distinct background finds hard to assess; but they are also typical stock in trade, at other points, of the working relationships affecting the operations of the physician himself.   While attempting to generalize only a few of these, Sullivan includes such cultural notions as the belief people are taught, in our society, "that they *ought not* need help."   In the frankly more religious atmosphere of nonliterate cultures, and often because many of these cultures stress cooperativeness in actual social relations, these constant necessities of propping up self-esteem are sometimes absent.   Benedict has contrasted two types of modern culture,—the guilt reactions of Western Europe, implicit in individualism and the Protestant ethic (a Horneyan notion as well), and the shame and social-expiation culture such as is posited for the Japanese in *The Chrysanthemum and the Sword*.   In our understanding of Japanese culture, the latter "sense of shame" comes within the guilt-framework. But even more important, there are cultures which produce less of the added effects of shame or guilt, or indeed a sense of foolish inadequacy, or defiant resentments.   It is fruitless to ask of ourselves *how much* these overtones are basic personality responses and how much they are culturally induced.   Anthropological studies, having a wide geographic range and intensive documentation, already indicate they are both at the same time.   The answer cannot be given in more precise quantitative or qualitative terms until anthropology and psychiatry truly collaborate.

Destructive emotions are found in inextricable combination in both the traditional cultural or group scene and in the context of personal lives.   From the point of view of mental health cross-culturally, these must be dealt with in the individual therapeutic situation, as well as in the field of preventive psychiatry.   The further idea Sullivan notes for our cultural stock in trade, namely that people must know themselves "and be able to see through others" in respect to motivation is as reprehensible in the form of probing on the part of the inexperienced as it is in the form of neatly rationalized systems of guarded suspiciousness in urban patients of Western provenience.   In turn, says Sullivan, the black and white, or airtight cultural value-concepts, like "good" versus "bad," "right" or "wrong," "the logical, right way," or fixed Horatio Alger notions of how people overcome limitations, mistakes, and misfortunes, impose burdens on the patient and often the unsuspecting physician which were not there originally. It is a fine line between an adjectival description of a patient's personality liabilities or lacks, (objectively defined failures in human relations) on the one hand, and a sense of hopelessness or defeat about his prognosis or management.   Unfortunately, because of our own perfectionistic emphases in cultural value system, that fine line is sometimes not there.[140]

Even in the initial acceptance of, and attitudes towards psychiatry and its various schools and positions, there are cultural differences in patients' set and response. B. H. Roberts and J. K. Myers, writing on religion and nationality in relation to mental illness as determined in the New Haven Study, point out several different rates of disorder in ethnic groups which agree largely with R. W. Hyde's findings, in Boston, in the Forties. The data for New Haven, in 1950, suggested that psychoneurotic disorders were more frequent among Jewish people, whereas the rate of affective disorders in this group had fallen to the average of the total population of those in treatment, public or private. Alcoholism was most prevalent among the Irish. Illnesses of senescence, and affective disorders were higher in the foreign-born; while psychoneuroses, under treatment, were higher in the native-born group.

The schizophrenias, or psychoses with mental deficiency were not related to these social variables. However, since the study was limited to those in treatment at a particular time in 1950, and does not include a community survey of families and individuals, such findings are to be scrutinized from a standpoint different from the data of Hyde and associates. The authors note, and this may well affect the above data, that Jewish cultural values are more accepting of and consistent with the tenets of psychoanalytic thought than are, say, those of Irish.

This fact must be reflected in higher rates of psychoneuroses among the Jewish people *if only those in treatment comprise the universe studied.* Yet this finding, while of no epidemiological importance, is nevertheless significant in another light. Where no conflict exists between doctrine or belief on the one hand, and the style of therapy utilized, then the rate of those so treated will rise with no reflection on incidence rates. Therapies prevailing in reference to mental illness have rarely been studied from the point of view of their appropriateness in a given cultural value system. Both the Hyde study and the Roberts-Myers' publication find that Italians have high rates of affective disorders and illnesses of senescence with Irish "devoid of any psychoneurotic disorders." However, Roberts and Myers stop to note in addition the artifacts of the cultural situation in which Irish may very little use the techniques of psychoanalysis. Italians, quite often to effect marriages or maintain family reputation, will conceal such blots on the escutcheon as illness, physical or mental, in a family, or may forego treatment, again for cultural reasons, in such early periods of life. Even the aged among the Italians may more frequently rely upon home care as respected and honored members of the family. Consequently, among Italians, the ultimates of a disease process of old age may take their toll.[141]

Knowledge of a cultural value system is important both in designing epidemiological or etiological research on mental disorders.   It is one thing to note, in evaluating research *results*, that a group of given cultural background are over-represented, or else not represented adequately in the kind of data that has been gathered; it is another step, however, to design the means for locating the incidence or prevalence of psychoneuroses in an Irish population which is, by and large, not under treatment.   Similarly, one must cross-check the apparent over-representation of Jewish population in private treatment against their possibly lesser representation in psychiatric institutions. Even so, these cultural and religious categories can be re-examined in the light of other variables, such as socio-economic range, generation level and acculturation phenomena, or adaptation of the group in a particular milieu. Even the facilities and types of treatment available have local or geographic reference, so that for our American regions, the Jewish data on psychoneurotic illnesses under private treatment might be expected to vary again in the Deep South or American Northwest.   By and large, Irish may also show a greater use of facilities in the New York and New Haven area, where facilities are plentiful and frequently under Catholic guidance.   The same variance would exist in the other south and west regions.   Until these qualifications are noted for resulting data, and circumvented, where possible, in research design, confusions of cultural variations with those that are clinical will abound.   The regional or community sample is the best antidote to this difficulty.

Confusions of clinic and culture exist in other areas as well.   On quite a different level of interpretation, there are those who assume without much psychiatric data that since nonliterate cultures are not instinctual paradises, or are not otherwise perfect in minimizing problems of adjustment, that they therefore constitute a limitless happy hunting ground for the discovery of illness typology. Such expectations are shattered often by the variance from conditions in modern cultures. A schizophrenic with paranoid reaction-formation from the cultures of the Northwest Coast of North America (Kwakiutl, Tlingit, Tsimshian, etc.) was actually not common, according to available evidence, in days before large-scale culture contact. Since then, more such cases have occurred, but apparently in no huge numbers and with no greater rate of incidence than marks the occasional case in the acculturated parts of African and other regions. The author worked with a complete sample of such cases in a federal institution, the Morningside Hospital and Clinic, and found no direct one-to-one correspondence of clinical cases with aboriginal cultures which had been termed "megalomaniac" by Ruth Benedict. Until such far-fetched confusions or identities of "culture" and "clinic" are eliminated, the psychiatric profession will continue to doubt anthropological discussions of cultural ways of life as modeled on clinical prototypes. No real or permanently useful discussions of cultural backgrounds and their influences on mental disorder are available under such impressionistic methods which do not discriminate statistically between the people in society who are reasonably well in any functional rating scheme, and those who function inadequately because of mental ills. Terms like schizoid, paranoid, megalomaniac, or oral, anal, and genital do not begin to describe the healthy functioning in any culture, let alone its probable failures. This, too, is a positive emphasis of the psychosocial position. Again, in clinical prototypes of cultural systems, we are dealing with descriptive shorthand, but in this case a shorthand unfortunately used in application to massive and traditional ways of life built up over time by countless generations of a people.

PART II

THE PSYCHOLOGY OF CULTURES
AND PEOPLES

III

THE PSYCHOLOGY OF CULTURE

IN AN EARLIER publication, the author stated:[142]

"... From the standpoint of anthropology, *what* is repressed, *who* are or who become cathected targets of projection or introjection, or *what role models* are available for sublimation, —all of these conditions are matters which vary with the culture. In the same way, cultural analysis explores *how* it is that dependent, controlling, rejecting, hostile or brutalizing human relationships can develop in a society, family, or organization. The same analysis may reveal how typical processes of positive or negative identification are begun within cultural settings by studying respondents, informants or even patients as to their background. The failures or successes of super-ego or ego functioning occur in precisely this context. Once such factors are adequately and sympathetically understood, then adequate keys to etiology, therapy and possibly prevention are furnished."

It is doubtful, therefore, that the study of individualized mechanisms of defense, in separate and isolated cases, is enough to throw light on such matters as "typical processes" of identification in a culture, common characteristics of projection or introjection, or on successful super-ego functioning. In addition to specific cultural factors in pathology discussed above for certain peoples and historical periods, there is the whole question of the values and attitudes affecting behavior variations in healthy functioning. We have, as D. Mackay pointed out for East Africa, little conception of normalcy as it varies with culture or of the relativity of the normal. While anthropological literature, in the main, has not attacked the problem from the point of view of psychiatry and its interests, it contains highly contrasting pictures of family and kin organization, differing patterns of child-rearing, parental roles, and the handling of inter-generation conflict, as well as surprisingly variable kinds of expressivity and constriction of emotions on the level of action or the level of fantasy.   Even the attitudes about physical and mental illness vary from culture to culture and thus affect both the discovery and the handling of illness.

In his abundant references to the psychopathology of everyday life, Freud showed clearly that defenses are used among the normally functioning, he himself offering a good part of the personal introspective material.   On the other hand, institutions for the mentally ill are full of persons firmly convinced of their normalcy in all details and showing, particularly in the schizophrenias, a monotonous sameness in denials of emotional problems.   So delicate are these emotional balances, and so extensive the protective and defensive mechanisms that at times an anxious distortion of reality to fit need-satisfying delusions becomes the actual "reality" for the patient. What Freud would call the "reinvesting of energy, the re-cathexis" does not always imply a reintegration of personality in which reality-testing starts up again on more productive and creative levels.   Defensive and protective processes are often self-defeating.   They not only exist in the normally functioning in vestigial form, but have various *degrees of organization and utilization* in the mentally ill.   One has only to think of particular kinds of productivity in some geniuses; the chaotic sexuality of Leonardo da Vinci, the hypersensitivity and masochism of Van Gogh and de Maupassant, and the wrecked lives of Utrillo, Toulouse-Lautrec, Paganini, or Arthur Schnitzler; we realize the difficulty of assigning a functional rating to total personality. In the famous seventh Chapter of his major work on dream analysis, Freud characteristically showed this difficulty as it applied to all men. At the same time, he also evidenced a greater interest in the comparison of neurotic and psychotic functioning as to *similarities in the kinds of defenses utilized*, than attention to the *differences in their organization and utilization*.

No doubt, as Rennie points out, "normal individuals" use defensive mechanisms in rudimentary form to cope with inner conflicts and exceptional life strains. At the same time, he suggests, careful diagnoses based on clinical, psychodynamic evidence and observation are all the more important in venturing prognoses or selecting therapeutic means. The *organization* of such mechanisms and their *degree of mobilization* in the spare adjustive machinery of all men constitute the outstanding differential factor with which therapy actually must deal. Consequently, this is one approach to *differences* in psychopathology, and one important for therapy. While the temptation is great to read off into the everyday life of "normal people" in a culture the same kinds and intensities of defense utilization as exist in clinical cases, these last occur only in pathological form among the ill of that culture. In exactly the same manner, the problem for social psychiatry is to trace how a kind of rudimentary defense mechanism characteristically originates in the setting of "normative" cultural behavior, and how typically, in given conflicts and strained circumstances, it becomes further adumbrated and intensified. Thus preventive psychiatry cannot omit the so-called normally-functioning of a society, and is best prepared by a cultural knowledge of their conflictual needs, environmental stresses, and perpetuated family and community problems.

Rough similarities in the kinds of protective or defensive mechanisms humans use do not necessarily imply identities in total personality organization or functioning for every individual of a given culture. Let us look again at the engaging simplicity which motivates Freud's major work on dream analysis.[143] By and large it assumes that the kinds of defenses at the disposal of "normal," neurotic and psychotic always originate in the same arenas of personal conflict, with the same action or purpose, the same effect, and presumably the selfsame conditions of environmental stress. As for dream symbolizations, some of which undergo little distortion, (others to quote Sullivan, showing parataxic or prototaxic disguises and points of reference), these are not systematically studied as to any possible social and cultural points of origin, different characteristic settings for different life periods, or in terms of *particular* kinds of displacement, condensation or repression. One is reminded of Sullivan's psychotic Italian patient whose father-authority symbol which "dominated" him was at one time "Columbus, admired and adventurous," later becoming The Big Man, and finally "any man." In this work, *The Interpretation of Dreams*, there is really little attention paid to neurophysiological problems like the physiology of sleep, sleep disturbances, or to social phenomena like the range of cultural fantasy materials. The variation by cultural background of distortion in different kinds of illness was not Freud's central interest. Yet it is a legitimate concern of psychotherapy. There have been no decisive or definitive studies on a cultural level of these remarkable languages of symbolization and imagination in the mentally ill. While psychoanalysis, then and now, typically subordinates questions of differential diagnosis and variable typology on a cultural basis to its more central interest in *pan-human mechanisms of psychological development*, it does so with insistence upon a particular kind of exploratory and interpretive technique in patients. This single elaborated methodology is geared primarily to certain kinds of neurotic illnesses found in Europe and America, and is sometimes peculiarly inappropriate to other illnesses in other cultures, and even to some life periods. Today one adds a concern for these assets or liabilities of a case.

To cite certain obvious examples, among the Ute Indians of Colorado, where dream analysis is the major shamanistic technique, this Freudian method of exploration is reality bounded and socially sanctioned within stated limits.[144] Sexual behavior also may be discussed freely and frankly. However, methods aimed at reducing periods of hospitalization in more serious illnesses of this or any culture, a problem in Freud's time as in ours, are not promoted by encouraging free associations in a rapidly disorganizing personality. Where essentially private languages are used by schizophrenics, should one devote endless time to following the neologistic language of a desperate delusion? If lack of control over impulsivity, whether it takes the form of an Irish patient's predilection for projecting fantasy, or an Italian's for more direct motility and acting out of emotions, are these not *harmful* modes of catharsis and *false* tactics of abreaction in serious illness to be guarded against? Only a fuller study of the assets or liabilities of the case, and therapeutic methods aimed differently from these impulses will produce personality reintegrations. Knowing how patients may typically react implies knowledge of their cultural backgrounds.

It is futile to select a single method as *the* therapeutic means. The etiological variations within such grand clusters of illness typology as "the schizophrenias" require further discrimination as to cultural background and the disorders of emotional communication must be investigated in terms of *the kind of symbolic and emotional language most often used* in each cultural setting. Certainly there are cultural ranges, if not fixations, which are systems of thought and action. The specific, individual case, always the start of significant research, may be grouped with others as to etiology and background factors. It is felt that such groupings and classifications are possibly more meaningful than the generous and all-embracing diagnostic labels.

While vast insights were developed in the Freudian movement, and in other psychiatric theories, the drive in the former movement towards a unitary theory of panhuman psychic development was premature. The universal theory did not adequately account for variations in human behavior across cultural lines, or between different disease processes, or even within a range of symbolic mechanisms of interpersonal communication. It had little to say about positive aspects of culture in interpersonal relations for creative and productive purposes. In this light it is curious that many anthropologists attracted to psychiatry (and several psychiatrists attracted to anthropological data) have settled upon theories of infantile disciplines to explain whole cultures in a highly simplistic fashion. If one goes beyond cultural and disease differentiation to an actual study of symbolic mechanisms resident in different types of families by matched samples of well and ill, the psychological impressionism disappears. As a matter of fact, in most existing studies, psychotic, psychoneurotic and "normal" are rarely distinguished, let alone sampled, matched for control of variables, or studied by family type at all.

In spite of this, one can speak of the existence of various useful therapeutic methods, and indeed, of the "peaceful coexistence in our times" of techniques which are in one case physiological, in another neurological, in another environmental or psychological. No one of these, as technique, type of analysis, or approach to human behavioral problems, is alone sufficient to cope with what

Malraux once called the human predicament in general. The fact is that man *is* an animal of great biological and psychic complexity. Exclusive reliance upon a single tool of analysis, whether biological or psychological, can be greatly misleading. On one level, that of the general psychic unity of mankind (popular in German anthropology in the time of Adolf Bastian), a rigid "Freudian" can overlook the crucial difference between an individual whose *past* defense structure can be maintained even where it now looks fragile, a second person capable of reeducation and a third who has already moved, or may move, full-arc from rigid and obsessive maintenance of constricted, hostile and compulsively-stereotyped relations with others, on to withdrawal, depersonalization feelings, further loss of reality contact and self-esteem to full projection of inner conflicts and delusional ideation. The former may be a way point, potentially, to the latter more disorganizing and paralyzing sort of illness, but the integrations are of three types, their styles of functioning quite different, and the three patients have needs, personality structures, defense organizations, and general adequacy for one kind of treatment or another that will vary.

In Kardiner's works, *The Psychological Frontiers of Society* and *The Individual and His Culture*, we learn that cultures also produce or promote forms of emotional expressivity, folklore, arts and religions, even where these have the character of group *projections*. Whether these are cultural safety valves, in the Freudian sense of displacements, compensations, or distortions, or whether they represent within the boundaries of modified Freudian theory, productive and creative urges, is, of course, a crucial question. Certainly the arts often exist far beyond the bounds of distortion, and may indeed transmit humor, insight, education, relaxation, or the creative mobilization of energies to those who benefit from them. Equally, it may be doubted whether religions, in the Durkheim sense of *a social institution*, or in Malinowski's of a force making for cultural integration are merely psychological excrescences of physiological urges or the inevitable results of infant disciplines. We may note variations among Mohammedans, Catholics, or Protestants, Buddhists, Jews, Shintoists or Animists depending on regional cultures. Religious psychology is not biologically or fatefully beyond good or evil.[145] It is highly probable that human defenses and uncertainties get established as modes of thought, emotion or action in the texture of whole cultures. But this applies to law, to economics, and to political structures as well as to the artistic and the religious. One has only to mention along with ritual compulsives and the work of imagination, hostile competitiveness, meaningless constrictions and taboos on positive or creative human expression, and the compulsive production and adherence to sterotypes. Where ritual interests are suffused with artistic or economic ones in cultures having little science and technology, or where shamanistic religions function in lieu of medicine and psychiatry, the anthropologist has little clear evidence of the projections being parataxic distortions. Perhaps this is why "primitives" have no Sundays or do have sincere and compelling forms of art connected with myth and ritual. Among them, it is frequently the large scale scientific and technical innovation that challenges religious forms.

On another level, that of emotional form and content in different cultures, the pan-human theory has further difficulties. When a certain number of Chinese schoolboys smile engagingly during a reprimand of the master, and mean by this the acme of respect and concern for their ineptitudes, there is some qualification upon the meaning of serious respect for all mortals. When an Apache Indian, in the white heat of uncontrolled anger, drops his voice to a scarcely audible whisper, he is about to convert verbal anger to serious assault. Dropping from a loud voice, or lowering the voice, means quite the opposite with us. When a tears-greeting in a third culture is accompanied by a copious flood of real tears, and the person doing the greeting falls weeping into the lap of a visitor, he is being assured of a hearty welcome, the utmost hospitality, and a positive attitude at his arrival. The language of emotions varies so markedly that a Masai warrior of standing will honor a young novice by spitting in his face. An Eskimo will show sincere concern and respect for the aged and infirm by abandoning them to die before they grow older. And a Siamese lady will show her breeding and respect for visitors by refraining from pointing her feet in their direction. Among the Tuaregs, noblewomen of the warrior caste frequently led men into battle or presided with the stringed instrument at medieval love courts; if the men, who wore the veils, accidentally showed their faces above or below the eyes, this was considered immodest in the extreme. Among the Japanese, where thwarted love led frequently to double suicides of the couple concerned, or where the chief item of classical fiction by the Lady Murasaki, *The Tale of Genji*, is a protracted account of courtly liaisons, assignations, and fervid letters of passion and feeling, the very notion of kissing in public is shameful and disgusting, whereas public nudity in town or village baths is a matter of no consequence. In Japanese hotels, even today, the most staid male guests are asked, with utmost decorum by equally staid chambermaids, if they wish to be undressed. Among the Ute Indians, female breasts have no sexual significance; and in another context of this culture the dead are best honored by Ute relatives forgetting them immediately. A visitor to Italian opera in the smaller locales of South Italy will witness an audience empathizing in a most emphatic and audible manner. And religious practitioners in a range of cultures do not worship supernaturals at a respectful distance; they control them, evoke them, imitate and incorporate them with pleadings, cajoling, commanding, and mimicry.

Just as there is no single language of appropriate emotions or the means to their expression, so no society is built, as Benedict implied in *Patterns of Culture*, out of one process of psychological selectivity from merely one range of emotional expression. Despite naive assumptions of wholly cooperative or wholly competitive cultures, none can be built forever on hostile, competitive lines, the Melanesian Dobuans to the contrary notwithstanding. In each culture, some unities and peer-group associations operate to facilitate creativity. It is interesting to read Benedict's picturing of the raw competitiveness of the Kwakiutl and in Middletown, and then to read Sapir's or Boas' account of the vast amount of cooperation within the *numaym* (bilateral kingroup) of the commoners in terms of whose labors the chief's potlatches (competitive give-aways) can only originate, or really ultimately benefit. In Boas' discussion, the background of these customs was in real warfare among coastal village sites. In Sapir's parallel descriptions of Northwest Coast social organization, the real economic privilege, along with the prestige symbols, is clearly described. Among the Nootka, *topati*, or prerogatives, are both real and tangible, as well as prestigeful. Under modern conditions, it is clear why both warfare has now ceased and yet group production and competition has continued. These social integrations of a cultural group are classified by the anthropologist, Radcliffe-Brown, who claimed them to be more beneficial in counteracting competitive and divisive incursions into social solidarity and mutual interest where they promote *closer* solidarity and cohesion. He regards them as being more important for human society in general where they become *wider* in effective extent.

This interest in the functional integration of social structures has become a dominant ideation of British social anthropology.   When even a highly segmented social structure like the Japanese of the Meiji period (with authoritarian controls, fixed classes, an outcaste *eta* group and attendant or buttressing custom and etiquette) contained, as John Embree showed in *Suye Mura*, remarkable patterns of mutual aid, social solidarity, village cooperativeness, and family unity, then clearly one may speak of social integrations which are segmented on one level and cooperative on another.

In one experiment unfortunately visited on Japanese-Americans, the values of social solidarity, cooperativeness, family unity, and organizational ability were clearly shown among Japanese who came primarily from rural and fishing villages of Hiroshima and Wakayama provinces.[146]   If the village level contains and defines these positive values, they may, for Japan as a whole, be widely represented in the common total of population.

In much the same way, when the anthropologist studies the folklore and arts of a people, he finds himself close to the channels of positive human expression as lived in a culture in its most enduring forms.   When we turn next to the more negative components of cultures, we find that the destructiveness, in Rado's sense, rarely accounts for the whole cultural tradition.   Stereotypes like passive-dependent Pueblo Indian, the paranoid Kwakiutl, and the hostile Dobuan fade from view.   In the cultural life of people, a compulsive adherence to stereotypes, a substitution of myth and delusion for reality, or a Nazi transformation of people into godly paranoids are, respectively, hostile gestures, cultural distortions, social aggressions and deadly fears which last only as long as a willful turning away from realities of world history can last.   When once they fall from the sheer weight of distortion, the social and cultural life of a people does not end, at least it has not as yet. In brief, whatever important qualities of character and temperament are characteristically developed in a cultural setting, they are found simultaneously on both levels of human action, the individual and the cultural. On the cultural level, most people in most cultures have the necessary modicum of functional good health. In cultures, as with individuals, only when this ceases to be the case are the dire predictions of a Toynbee then in order.

However, the analogy of culture and the individual must end here. The two phenomena are different. The tendency of R. H. Lowie in his *Social Organization* or of Malinowski in much of his writing to ascribe a biological need basis to culture points to a truth, but not the whole truth. Other human gregarious needs, beyond the confines of individual biology, are supplied by culture. The arts, science, religion, philosophy, relaxation and recreation supplement sexual, nutritive, shelter and protection requirements of man. The various social, religious, artistic and other organizations by which these are achieved constitute a first and additional step in analysis which goes beyond biological man and which immediately separates him from his primate brethren. When we proceed to the level of communication and expression in whole cultures, the latter become irreducible to individual personalities. More careful statistical methods of grouping and estimating personality variations are then necessitated.

In anthropology, the clinical model of a particular kind of personality disorder has too often provided a yardstick for assessing "culture and personality." Types of aberrancy common in Western European and American cultures erroneously provide "clues" to the understanding not merely of clinical typologies, but cultural ones as well. By claiming a close correspondence between the clinical model showing predisposition towards extreme forms of psychotic behavior and adult personality, the culture is so stereotyped.[147]   Edward Sapir, who founded culture and personality research in anthropology, warned repeatedly against viewing cultures, by simple analogy, as being obsessive, hysterical, paranoid, and the like.[148]   While the cross-cultural comparisons can probably never end in a purely relativistic set of conclusions, and the "normalcy" of one become the aberration of another, neither can they be reduced by analogy to a clinical model of a personality disorder.   Comparisons of the prevalent psychopathology developed in cultural frameworks show these to differ, but here prevalence or incidence must not be assumed.   The epidemiological yardstick is the number of persons of given biological and social characteristics becoming ill in a given period of time.   Anthropologists interested in culture and personality must recognize this principle of the medical and health sciences.

In the same fashion, it is doubtful whether data on isolated cultures, or isolated humans in a non-representative series, can furnish the kind of information required to establish a science relating to the psychology of cultures and peoples.   Epidemiological exactitude is one necessity, but cross-cultural comparison, controlling variables other than the cultural is likewise desirable.   There is face validity to the proposition that humans, living in families and social groups of a culture, fall into a continuum from well to ill.   Their interpersonal communications, with language or with other symbolic means commonly defined, add to the basic determinants of their biological natures and material culture all those elements of meaning and emotion, character and temperament which make them what they are.   While it is common to speak of these cultural affairs as the traditional superstructure of social living, traditions change and "super-structure" need not connote remoteness.

Human organization and functioning, in social and cultural contexts, is more than bodily need and physical impulse. One has only to think of the Navajo who will starve rather than eat fish, or the broken taboo which in Polynesia should lead, and often does, to death. In exactly this sense of cultural complexity to regulate behavior by non-biological proscriptions and prescribed conduct, culture becomes irreducible to mechanisms of defense (the Freudian view), or to neat, patented resolutions of all conflict. For most persons, the invitation to all sorts of cultural activity is accepted unconsciously and easily, and the inevitable coin of the realm of behavior is cultural coin even without their examination of it. However, while personal meanings, conscious or unconscious, intrude into this well-populated area of social personality, they do not ordinarily alter or change the course of traditional, "normal" functioning. Still less, do the personal meanings disrupt or swerve a history built up by countless generations. An individual's "culture" or sub-culture may vary uniquely from these norms with hardly a ripple in the stream of history. Cultural analysis is always this first necessary and preliminary bow to the human scene at its most commonplace. When the generic cultural factors are established, there are then reference points or norms *against which personalized psychologies can be studied.* In such studies, the individual is observed in his actual human and social relationships within patterns that are never wholly of his making. If we are to know him at all, his meanings and those larger meanings which are cultural play as light and shadow, foreground and background, or as texture and form constituting the complete picture.

The chief limitation of the Freudian view is that it was not geared to these necessities of a larger perspective. Partly for this reason, as Kluckhohn has implied, cultural anthropology was most often associated with the modified, more recent wings of the psychoanalytic movement.[149] However, both fields historically establish earlier relationships in subject matter and method. Psychoanalytic theory as first promulgated by Freud and his circle was in agreement with the basic position and even the data of Nineteenth Century anthropology. In both, originally, the conception of man's mind (and his culture *as consequence*) were envisaged as developing in a biologically predetermined evolution through stages from infancy to maturity. In both, the legacy of this childhood and of man's early social development were found in survivals to later stages. Spencerians spoke of savagery as the childhood of man, calling this early development a time of simple, undifferentiated impulse and biologically conditioned action. Psychoanalysis spoke of the neurotic as "regressed to primitive stages" of thought. In one early psychoanalytic system, *the* child was virtually caricatured as rehearsing the past of his "race" by virtue of a primordial "mass psyche" imbedded in him. In this fatefully pessimistic system, the savage, the child, and the neurotic were compared, as fantasy-ridden, a prey to physical impulse. Children and the adults of remote cultures were said to be emotionally and morally "undifferentiated," or in Spencerian terms, naively egoistic, irrational, uncooperative, and incapable of finer discriminations. The appropriateness of childhood fantasy in the development of a more adult statement of human insight and imagination, or the uses of childhood confusions in the absence of full, mature information; their spontaneous impulses in the presence of rapid growth and high energy utilization, all of these factors in child maturation were not fully appreciated in this humorless drive towards a system. In *The Problem of Lay Analysis*, Freud asks seriously whether the "soul-life" of present day children does not reflect "the same archaic moments" that prevailed "at the time of early civilizations." The answer from both psychology and anthropology has long been an emphatic negative.

Today, we see the simplicity of both schemes in anthropology and psychoanalysis as reflecting the success of Darwinism in the decade before. The popularity, in Freud's day, of such highly systematized and imaginative works as Andrew Lang and Atkinson's *Social Origins and Primal Law* are noted as a chief source of his own *Totem and Taboo* in their immistakable similarity. This work, by Andrew Lang and J. J. Atkinson, was published in 1903, and antedated by a dozen years Freud's *Totem and Taboo* which belongs to the period 1912-1913. In it, a "pre-totemic race" unaware of incest or exogamy is first posited along with the familiar promiscuous Cyclopean horde, the dominance of the older men, and the jealousy of a youthful band of classificatory kin-brothers. Next come the inevitable parricidal acts. With the functioning of guilt mechanisms and ritual displacements is born the totemistic injunction against killing and eating an ancestral animal and symbolic figure. Along with these guilts and rituals emerge incest regulation, exogamy, religion and ethics in the real functioning social world. No wonder J. C. Flügel, in his *Freudian Mechanisms as Factors in Moral Development*, could, with a sense of security about his anthropological data, incorporate this same theme of equating the primitive, the child, and the neurotic. As late as 1924, in his address before the Royal Anthropological Institute in London, Ernest Jones reiterated the same points.

In place of mental stages, biological and mental in essence, one today notes the important effects of culture upon individuals throughout the life course. Instead of an unvarying notion of child development, transcending cultures and world history back to an "archaic past," today we consider developmental needs of children in relation to cultural and social situations, unconnected to a hypostatized "primitive mind." Specific background factors and influences can be tested for their effects upon mental, emotional and ethical growth. Mind, as such, is in one sense mental functioning, to be sure, but it is even more crucially an *organization* of beliefs, attitudes, perceptions, meanings and emotions derived from social and interpersonal experiences in a particular setting. In place of defenses that mark *stages* of mental functioning, the anthropologist adds a broader category, namely the typical patterns of response and expressivity that individuals of a culture utilize in the most characteristic business of living. These, of course, include defenses. But in addition they include patterns of response to infant and child-rearing methods, to family and kinship organization, to parental roles and the handling of inter-generation conflict, and to the more subtle influences in any culture which promote or constrict the handling of emotions, impulses, or attitudes. Terms like education, physical or mental illness, sexual expression, or work and leisure, all connote mental processes. Since a culture, by its very nature, will provide characteristic modes of harnessing human energy and will relate typical problems to typical solutions, no meaningful life experiences within its boundaries, whether birth, growth, maturation, or death, are free from its affective charges. The latter, far from occurring only in an individual arena of unique "experience," are bound inevitably to human interrelationships, or in short, to the realities imposed upon individuals by group phenomena. Commonly defined meanings and sanctioned behavior favored by the group in its manner of maintaining itself or its members affect all mankind.

In this light, the expressive symbolism and folk art of a given culture has a function and type of expressivity impossible to disconnect from the realities, or "conditions," of the culture. To cite a single example, in hunting and gathering societies marked by marginal living (Australian,

African Bushman, South American Siriono, American Ute and Apache) the very nomadism means there will be no adjustment of means to remote ends. Ceremonies are often dramatic or mimetic of nature, and religion involves direct contacts with an animated (we say animistic), highly anthropomorphic set of supernaturals. All this John Dewey noted in his *Philosophy and Civilization* where he discussed such variations. The contrast to Indian Pueblos and their ceremonial of group formation with its air of sculptural inevitability and the *ethos* of restraint, cooperation and sobriety was noted both by Dewey and Ruth Benedict and applied by the latter to the whole society. These are people with priesthoods; not, as with the hunters and gatherers, people who act directly. Instead they plant, and wait, and pray. They live as a village with sanctions against competitiveness. And their cultures have no more in common with hunters and gatherers than they have in common with Italian, German, Irish, or Hungarian. They leave to those of the list labeled nomadic all the dramatic or vividly mimetic elements in religious ceremonies.

These comparisons and the typology implied in modern cultural anthropology are far from Freud's source of stages in work by Lang and Atkinson. In *Social Origins and Primal Law*, or in Freud's other sources, such as Frazer's *Golden Bough*, imaginative authors had postulated the existence of what they termed a Cyclopean, original "family" in earliest times. They did so not to describe a given known culture, but to categorize several. Dominant males in possession of the females, until vanquished and slain by younger males, do not characterize the male population of any known culture. The parallel of Nineteenth Century anthropology to the Oedipus myth or to *Totem and Taboo* is clear, but no psychology of any individual or any culture has been depicted. Even totemism as the thinly-veiled ritual projection of a life-drama does not describe any totemistic people. In the Freudian version, both parricide and incest occur, followed by poignant regret. Culture, religion, morality and a social sense flow from this more lurid and phylogenetic version of Oedipus. The account is poetic, and one anthropological reviewer, Goldenweiser, suggested Freud only poetically over-embroidered an imaginative elaboration. In some circles the same embroidering still continues, however. Culture has appeared on the scene as the merest epiphenomenon. It becomes a consequence of psychology, not a cause.

Others, like Rank and Róheim, saw Oedipal structure growing out of ontogenetic factors, birth-trauma or "resistance against" cellular fission processes in the embryo. Such bizarre psycho-biological theories signalized the danger of moving a theory of cultural behavior *away from* legitimate concerns of social psychiatry and *in the direction* of an ontological straightjacket. By the 1920's, when English translations of *Totem and Taboo* were being reviewed, Kroeber, accepting Freudian mechanisms like repression, regression, or sublimation, nevertheless pointed out that no known culture started on a sheer libidinal premise of dominant male strength. One might have added that in culture, with weapons and tools, all Goliaths have their Davids; others simply noted the frequently *fixed* monogamic marital forms in the simplest known peoples (whether Australians, or Andaman Islanders who lacked fire). While S. Zuckerman's studies of social functioning, in *The Social Life of Monkeys and Apes*, correspond to "primitive life" according to Freud or Lang and Atkinson, the simplest human cultures do not. Instead, the family and exogamy of one sort or another always prevail.

Totem and Taboo was translated during World War I. Freud, in the *Problem of Lay Analysis* could note that Theodore Reik and Géza Róheim, the ethnologist, "have taken up the line of thought . . . developed in *Totem and Taboo* and, in a series of important works have extended or corrected it." While Freud was right in the assertion that Rank, Róheim and others were extending his theories beyond *Totem and Taboo*, it was apparent that they were modifying these in a more clearly ethnological direction. Today *Totem and Taboo* can only be reviewed as poetic fantasy.

The deluge came in the 1920's. Besides the sharply critical reviews of *Totem and Taboo* by Kroeber and Goldenweiser, a third anthropologist, Malinowski, then in England, published a series of extended studies of a Melanesian people, the Trobriand Islanders. One of these volumes, *Sex and Repression*, was devoted to a masterful rebuttal of *Totem and Taboo*. In brief, as Kroeber had suggested, libidinal attachments and revulsions were not always charted as in the family of Oedipus Rex or Austrian Vienna. In the Trobriands, there was no father-authoritarian. The word for father there meant *tamakava*, "stranger in my village," a village under a matrilineal kinship system. While father was a cherishing companion for an infant, male or female, the mother's brother and his kin were feared from adolescence on by either girl or boy in an economy which centered in a maternal uncle's needs, demands and orders. The subsequent discussion of different kinds of family constellations the world over was a healthy revision of Freud's fixed stages, single origin point, and uniform psychodynamics throughout the world. Perhaps no discussion of culture was more prone to regard culture as an afterthought, an epiphenomenon, than Freud's in *Totem and Taboo* and none shattered as dramatically against the hard facts of cultural relativity.

However, Freud's discussion of the presence of emotional mechanisms connected with family structure (although of one type), of sex role identification, of child training or conditioning, and of the affective importance of one kind of family functioning were still of tremendous value. Even if the role of culture was hopelessly confused with a resultant of innate and inevitable psychological processes, and even though fixed, rigid modes of behavior were referred to "mass psyche" phylogenetically derived, the dynamic system soon proved flexible enough for useful modifications. While Karl Abraham enthused over the response of language (its emphasis on gender), to the Oedipal situation, anthropologists piled up evidence from a hundred languages (Algonquin, Athabaskan, Hungarian, and Bantu) to the effect that sex gender was often not the system of classification. While *Totem and Taboo* had set a dead stamp on all human behavior, later psychiatrists of a modified psychoanalytic persuasion, like James Clark Moloney, the Leightons, Joseph and Murray, were willing to go to other cultural scenes to study the actual and variable behavior of human beings.

Following critiques of *Totem and Taboo*, Freud revised his system in *The Ego and The Id*. This volume is of fundamental importance in the Freudian system because it explicitly stated a turning point, in which, to ego, id, and ego-ideal formulations was added the super-ego. The super-ego, the new element, was phrased ultimately as "the heir of the Oedipus complex, and represents ethical standards of mankind." This bowing out of Oedipus, and the substitution of an initial formulation on cultural value systems, was most important as an insight into personality backgrounds, even though it never came to be used for extending research perspectives self-consciously in the direction of social personality concepts.

In this new work, Freud's ego-ideal formulations are of interest as for example: "The tension between the demands of conscience and the actual attainments of the ego is experienced as a sense of guilt." In another place Freud asserts, "Social feelings rest on a foundation of identification with others, on the basis of an ego-ideal in *common* with them." What is common and shared? The answer is certainly cultural experience and values. No longer is this simply an individual psychology or individualized psychiatry. What Clara Thompson refers to in her book on psychoanalysis, where she marshals the trends toward what she calls the healthy"revisionists" of orthodox Freudianism by alluding to Horney, Fromm and Sullivan is exactly this type of theoretical revision. It is what Fromm develops in his concept of social character, or Sullivan in his frequent references to social relations.

In anthropology, the same trends have been noticeable. Culture, as generator and judge of the normal and abnormal in behavior, is no idle reification once we realize that real cultures, real sub-cultures and real people lie at the heart of the system. A personality, as Sapir once put it, "is carved out by the subtle interactions of those systems of ideas characteristic of a culture as a whole, as well as those systems of ideas which get established for the individual through more special types of participation with the physical and psychological needs of the individual organism." These Sapir calls "individual sub-cultures." They are Freud's egos. Sapir's culture as a whole is Freud's ego-ideal. Sapir goes on, we think to more crucial statements of what is involved in the interrelation of culture and mental illness. Rather than a one-to-one relationship, he writes as follows: "The personal meaning of the symbolisms of an individual's sub-culture are constantly being reaffirmed by society, or at least he likes to think they are. When they obviously cease to be, he loses his orientation— a system of sorts remains and causes his alienation from an impossible world."

What is needed to fill the framework of interdisciplinary

collaboration are two things beyond the uses of anthropology and psychiatry which Sapir implies. One is the necessity for psychiatry systematically to gather data on social and cultural backgrounds and systems of meaning which configure always in the background of real cases. The second is the necessity for anthropology to become sensitized not merely to the cultural backgrounds from which cases emerge, but to the typical modalities of mental functioning in human beings. The common ground we refer to, simply, as psychodynamics, requires, in other words, adequate medical psychiatric analysis of real people and real cases against a background of cultural understanding.

One final word. Anthropology speaks often of the "unconscious patterning of behavior in society" (the title of a famous paper of Sapir). A primitive is unconscious of the grammar of the language he speaks—though it is there; of kinship systems having symmetry, though they have; or of regularities in many realms of behavior. Besides the importance of unconscious processes—for both fields— there is the point that much of the content of culture, like the content of minds, is symbolic: the X that stands for functions, activities, movements, and expressions of human energy which are cultural in the first instance. The dream, the image, the belief, the action pattern are, in the individual, most often symbols in terms of which activity is expressed and lives are lived.

Obviously, defense mechanisms may figure in this study, but must be recognized as developing, if at all, within the framework of a larger conception of ego-organization which is culturally variable and corresponds roughly to the Sherif-Cantril psychology of ego-involvements. Cognitive *attitudes*, to judge by the enormous data of psychiatry, influence both cognition and perception on the level of the way in which persons of different culture interpret events, see objects or hear sounds within the normal range. In like manner, where distortions of events, or hallucinatory behavior occurs, as in the schizophrenias, cognitive attitudes have undergone distinctive changes. In the perception project of the Menninger Clinic, George S. Klein, Philip Holtzman and Diana Laskin write as follows:[150]

". . . Much of our work assumes that ego organization (*id* becoming 'secondary,' M. K. O.) is in part a network of controls organized to modulate claims of drive and reality. In psychoanalytic theory, impulse control has been discussed mainly in terms of defense. It seemed important to investigate the possible function of cognitive controls observed in our laboratory situation for the delay and discharge of need-tension. The question is relevant also to the general issue of structural constraints upon the directive influence of needs. Thus a series of experiments demonstrate that the effects exerted by the need in perceptual-associative behavior are distinctly different where the cognitive attitudes and adaptive problems vary. These studies and others seem to suggest that a wide variety of controls, *of which defenses may only be one form* (My italics, M.K.O.) *condition the working of need and drive and behavior*. These studies have contributed to our attempts to establish more explicit links to the psychoanalytic framework. For instance, it does not seem likely that the concept of defense, even 'autonomous' defense in the psychoanalytic literature is wholly adequate to describe the regulative strategies that subjects have shown in our perceptual tasks."

While several authors, Heinz Hartmann,[151] Ernst Kris,[152] and David Rapaport,[153] in their writings on ego-autonomy and problems of human adaptation, have tended to speak of personality functions not exclusively related to conflicting drives, Klein and his associates have attacked problems in perception and cognition as being not merely autonomous, but as being "themselves idiosyncratically organized within peoples into 'styles' or regulative principles."

The problem may not be whether Italians or Irish become entangled in personal conflicts, or repress, but rather *what* and equally important, *how* they repress, *how* they convert energies or direct them, and *what* cognitive attitudes and outlooks motivate them. These regulatory and control functions, no matter how much they become internalized in individual personality, have, as outer limits the cultural backgrounds, themselves uniquely organized into "styles and regulative principles." Although there is no need to assume a one-to-one correlation between the regulative principles and styles of thought, attitude and emotion in a culture and among its component individuals, we can still seek in each individual, as indeed psychiatry does, the really constructive forces or the assets within him, and note where these provide a bridge back to culturally shared traits. At the same time, what Fromm has called the "culturally patterned defect," (the pathological *tendencies* which a combination of cultural and psychiatric method may bring to light even in the study of the so-called normal) represents one set of factors in terms of which goal-selection, role fulfillment, concepts and cognitive attitudes, and even styles of emotional expression will necessarily vary. Thus a culture which is, at the present point in history, widely predisposing to conditions that breed disturbances in one's relations to others, or in the self-identification, goal orientation, family and social roles of the sexes and status groups within its social matrices, will reap the consequences of widespread compulsions, almost obsessional fears, patterned hostilities, and conflicting sets of motives. When these operate from individual to individual, they become reflected in the variances of incidence and types of disorder we have seen exist historically in the annals of human maladjustment.

In a more positive sense, every people and culture bring their own gifted solutions, their own unifying philosophy, to each individual at any point in his history. A person may give to this life-way, or this world view, his own interpretation in its affective dimensions. But he can no more create it from the outset than any one individual can design from the whole cloth of personalized abstractions any cultural product. If he can synthesize and integrate ideas, perceptions and emotions at all, he must do so in a manner and with an interpretation culled from experience in a larger more or less systematic patterning of human reactions about him. These premises of behavior and human relations are not learned by rote, and it is fruitless to assume as Hsu has done,[154] that in one culture a mechanism like repression generally operates, while in another suppression alone is the touchstone of existence.

Rather the regulatory controls, the styles of expression, the ordained goals and social role behavior are defined within the definition of the situation (its meanings and communicated symbols) long before anyone of us is privileged to select and construct a life pattern, or indeed, add personal understanding and interpretation to it. These dominant conceptions and assumptions of a culture, its group aspirations, religious lore, science, technique, custom, and ethical code may be internalized through unconscious habit in consistent patterns, as presumed by Benedict in *Patterns of Culture*, or they may contain the very inconsistencies, conflicts, outlines and demarcations which make a strain towards consistency more difficult in the individual case. It is the latter which defines cultural psychopathology, the culturally patterned defect, not the existence of one clinically defined type of aberration, deposited in the culture initially and then discovered by a selective description. Culture and psychology do not stand in even relationship, as effect and cause, cause and effect. While the way of life of a people may achieve internal coherence and unconscious canons of choice develop within it, culture is still an instrument in the adjustment of man and nature which mediates to achieve control, solve the problems of social conduct, economy, politics, religion and philosophy, and regulate behavior.

Any concept of national character, like any other concept, is real only insofar as it investigates, understands and communicates the dynamic working of a kind, or kinds of phenomena. If the individual and his culture are more than "interacting," in the language of early Twentieth Century sociology, and it appears that they are, then the structure of a personality and that of the culture from which it emanates, are caught in the same contexts, face the same problems, and develop the same general patterns and modes of action as solutions. Basic to any discussion of psychodynamics in a person are the modalities, biological, psychological, and social, governing the workings of need, drive and behavior. Over-individualized psychological systems minimize such central tendencies. Central tendencies, whether biological, or psychological and social, govern the workings of need, drive and behavior on the interpersonal cultural level as well. Descriptions of cultural patterns, as simplified statements of sculptured, inevitable ways of life do not fully explore these tendencies. When the actual dynamics of groups forming a cultural system are studied in terms more closely corresponding to need, drive, behavior, and the regulation of conduct, a psychology of peoples and cultures then becomes possible.

IV

CULTURE AND PSYCHIATRY

HAVING REVIEWED much of the relevant literature in social psychiatry, we are now in a position to state simply some basic propositions of this emerging interdisciplinary science. It is significant that its drive and direction is towards a generalizing behavioral science of man. As such, the classic interests of psychiatry in diagnosis and treatment are linked with considerations of the prevention or mitigation of mental disorders in sociocultural groups, and in improvements from an epidemiological point of view in the range of adjustment or adaptation of persons not functioning at optimum levels of health and creativity.

As we have seen, enormous descriptive and analytic problems concerning human behavior are involved. Only recently has the attack upon these problems included notions of man, not merely as a creature of biology and physiology responsive to overtones of his psychological existence, but as a social and cultural animal. As such, humans are equally responsive to cultural evaluations and attitudes as these impinge through family systems, art, religion, science, work and leisure, or even politics. These institutions of a culture or sub-culture are themselves unconsciously patterned into typical ways of thinking, acting and believing, but as custom and belief at its most commonplace they are constant in their influence on conscious and unconscious functioning as well. In simplest formulation, the texture of our conscious existence and the fabric of unconscious motivation, our daily lives so to speak, are constantly affected by larger patterns of behavior.

195

All humans therefore speak a necessary common language of survival and adaptation, viewing events as "beneficial," or "deleterious," or possibly "neutral," "inconsequential" and of no concern. The gregarious nature of the human primate, and his ability to communicate ordinarily in symbols which are cultural in the first instance, subject him immediately to all the conditions and consequences of such communication. As internal communication, in conflict *with himself*, the Freudian movement has brilliantly plotted a part of the course of personal entanglements, often with too little awareness of the relativity and the difference in symbols, attitudes, standards and evaluations which are measured differently from culture to culture. Therefore, even the internal conflicts, involving the regulatory and controlling tactics, and in Freudian language, "the defenses," are staged in quite different arenas of operation and expression.

Apart from these modifications of Freudian theory now in order, dispelling its fatalistic, narrow constriction into one culture scene, a second expansion of the theory long overdue is the relationship between internal conflicts in communication and the external world which influences them. The distinction here is not simply Jungian, the introvert and extravert dichotomies still centered in the individual; by pointing out the inevitable relationship between the inner and outer worlds of human beings, we involve ourselves in an analysis, on cultural and psychiatric grounds, of basic human values and the relative standards of normality which exist from culture to culture.

Consider, for a moment, the sense of communicating with others as discussed by Harry Stack Sullivan. These communications are not based solely, as he suggested, on an awareness of a common humanity in two or more persons, though of course this consciousness of humanity is of initial and prime importance. Self-object relations, or self-other conceptions require as an immediate part of external objectivity, a *specific* perception and cognitive evaluation of human *actions* or events without distortion and with reasonable possibility of the prediction of behavior in others. The contrary sense of isolation and loneliness reflect both this disturbed awareness, and the distortions in communication, certainly between inner and outer worlds. But schizoid withdrawal and its extreme isolation are no direct and accurate portrayals of the same state of communications, perceptions, and cognitive evaluations in the real world.

This fear of others, or of the consequences of one's own hostile motivations, stem from experiences which slowly and relentlessly destroy a sense of identity and of common humanity with others. Yet in cultures if the same sense of identity and humanity is tenuous, then the conditions within the culture help erect a towering barrier which can only connote the speeding of separation from others, or in Sullivan's language, the following of disjunctive relations. The helplessness of hostile motility disturbances in extreme fear and anger, or the individual reintegrations on new fantasy levels are not built unaided in family settings alone. They may be aimed at what seem to be the capacities for internal objectivity and self-esteem, or may be antisocial or asocial, depending on the discrete or specific symptomatology. But nevertheless, when we say such disordered and ill persons are no longer acting and thinking in terms of positive cultural values or normative human attributes, we mean fundamentally that not only have communications broken down in the individual or in the family, but that cultural norm and social group also allowed the sphere of their operations to become wholly internalized and incoherent. Thus the person partly is removed from *both* the contact with sustaining *cultural realities* and deprived of the ability *to adjust to gross environ-*

ment with perceptions and cognitive attitudes dedicated to healthy survival.

The curious thing about cultural realities, which vary within types or limits and never achieve abnormal integration wholly is that they affect individual conditioning processes. Basic human cognitive, perceptual and attitudinal equipment varies. Both this equipment and the norms of most cultures are inclined towards survival and healthy adjustment and are ordinarily, in the normative conduct of most people, so intended. Even the most violently anti-social symptomatology, like sociopathic disorder and extreme forms of paranoid schizophrenia in our own culture, or *amok* in Malaysia, rarely point to total genuine regressions and complete loss of contact or communication. Such individuals have, indeed, lost a cultural coloring, or broken completely from a pattern of certain kinds of self-other conceptualizations. But in a negative sense, they reflect the cultural stress system. It is likely in the passive forms of illness (the automatic obedience disorders, marked by lack of will, weak ego-organization, echolalia or echopraxia, *latah*, or "Arctic hysteria"), that each of these wide ranges of disorder are frantic attempts to organize autistic behaviour patterns and methods of communication and symbolization as a typical resort of certain cultural stress systems. All such illnesses do, in reality, reflect cultural demoralization. The distinction between health, on the one hand, and one typical form or another of illness in a culture is not merely between those who communicate, and those who do not, or those who fulfill needs, and those who have been thwarted. In each case, though quite opposite paths of symbolization, adjustment, and communication have been utilized, *both have derived from different aspects of the cultural realities*. In the one case, the adjustment of internal necessities and external conditions has been medi-

ated by regulative principles, defenses, modes of communication, and cultural symbols and values pressed in the
service of healthy adjustment.   In the other, with the
same modes of communication at his disposal and the
same range of symbols to draw from, the values, cognitive
attitudes, regulative principles, percepts and defenses have
been critically affected by the stresses inherent in the cultural scene.   In the most serious illnesses, we see an individual drawn finally into lines of conflict that are internal
to be sure, but mark a warfare between the self and "those
others" now dimly perceived, distorted, misunderstood
and hated as values and standards attenuate, grow weak,
and lose their persuasive quality.   We may thus speak not
only of weaknesses in individuals and in families, but in
cultural values.

The fear, in social science and psychiatry, of dealing
with values-systematizations, as if man were merely the
prey of irrational and psychological forces is a sign of our
culture and our times.   Many have been taught to feel
helpless before impersonal mechanistic forces.   Wars have
not mitigated these feelings.   In our mass-production,
highly-specialized, anonymous, and distantly regulated
mode of life (all of which David Riesman in *The Lonely
Crowd* designates as "other directed" standards of living),
we cannot see the interpenetration of particular kinds of
essentially human values with the potentialities of a richer
social and cultural life.   We sense a sameness in social and
cultural experience for all men, when, indeed, either history or travel would convince us of change and diversity.
Our problems and solutions in human psychology are
not always repeatable in history nor reduplicated across
the earth's surface.

These differing incidence rates of mental disorder and
psychosomatic illness are not matters of group biological
characteristics like race.   Essential hypertension in malig-

nant form is rare among unacculturated Negro peoples of Africa, but relatively common among American Negroes. A variation by historical period has also been noted in mental illnesses like the Dancing Manias of the Middle Ages which are rare today. Different *forms* of schizophrenic illness are characteristic of different parts of the world. We have suggested that varying culture standards, values and ways of life are responsible for this regional and group differentiation. In so doing, we have combined certain brilliant insights of the Freudian movement with clinical and social data stemming from post-Freudian anthropological and psychiatric movements. Our position has been close to that of Wegrocki who states,[155] "Obviously abnormal behavior is *called* abnormal because it deviates from the behavior of the general group." However, it is not the fact of deviation from a norm, but a causal background in the breakdown of adaptive functioning and regulatory principles *in reactions to stress*. Wegrocki does not call Plains Indian visions abnormal, for instance, but calls those of the schizophrenic in whatever culture by this term, stating that the two behaviors may *seem analogous*, but that they are *not homologous*. The essential difference Wegrocki sees in a tendency of abnormal behavior "to choose a type of reaction which represents an escape from a conflict-producing situation." Thus, it is not "a mechanism that is abnormal; it is its function which determines its abnormality." One could add that the kinds of conflict typical in a given society and family system will favor the functioning of certain mechanisms. Apparently, total personality function in the totality of a cultural context is the point at which to locate the difference between normal and aberrant.

If a mechanism like withdrawal (and repression of a sense of indentification with others, as a human being) is so basic a response pattern in a prevalent illness, it will reduce cultural contacts to the barest minimum. To note that a process of abnormality is in motion seems unnecessary. Any society may contain, in this sense, its noncultural, aberrant types. But not all societies and cultures show withdrawal symptomatology in such abundance. These persons, to be statistically significant at all in the meaning of deviancy "from the behavior of the general group" must be responding according to reaction *patterns* (not identities) which force certain kinds of dislocation of need, drive, behavior, and impulsivity-regulation to the fore, in which for the ultimate forms of disorder, cognitive attitude and adaptive behavior undergo distortion under the pressures of a wide number of traumatic agents: anxiety, hostility, and a sense of alienation among them. In another society, brief confusional states may be the more classical defense mechanism.

What LaBarre has called the ability of man "to be spectacularly wrong and wrong over long spans of space and time" has led him in his recent work, *The Human Animal*, into a style of thinking identical with that of Ruth Benedict. There is no discernible difference, writes LaBarre, in the content of a culture and a psychosis.[156] While the number of respective "communicants" in the normative case may be fifty million, and in the other aberrant situation of a mental disorder showing withdrawal it is always one, LaBarre notes quixotically that both are qualitatively based on symbol-systems. So is culture based upon the most positive characteristics of human beings without all cultures at all times evidencing this. Granted the same array of symbols "at disposal," the adaptive means and functions are forced into patterns destructive of enduring human relationships only in psychotics. To group one aspect of cause (the culture) with its consequence, the prevailing form of disorder, is highly misleading. Yet LaBarre presumes both culture and psychosis allay anxiety. The only difference he discerns is that the schizophrenic is "oriented relatively to the 'inside'," an amazing oversimplification, whereas the scientist, for example, is oriented "to the 'outside' of his organism." LaBarre's noncultural and nonpsychological usages of words like "know," "orient," and "symbol" suggest that the system cannot discover the actual contexts of normal and aberrant behavior since it has no reference to scientifically viable concepts of conditioning, motivation or function in either an anthropological or psychiatric sense. The reduction of culture to psychosis follows, as it does in so many systems because it is not based on acceptable scientific proof of obvious differences between the two phenomena.

The actual fact about the culture-personality interrelation is that the relationship is valid only if normal behavior can be related to the positive values of a culture and the disordered *in* a culture to its stress system. This requires properly weighting the enormous effects of culture in its relationship to individual members of a society. One contemporary American philosopher, Feibleman, has spoken of cultures as "wholes like organisms, *at least in the sense that they consist in something more* than the sum of their parts."[157] In this sense of larger, over-arching values or value orientations, Kluckhohn has stated a value-orientation may be defined as a "generalized and organized conception, influencing behavior, of nature, of man's place in it, of man's relation to man, and of the desirable and nondesirable as they may relate to man-environment and interhuman relations."[158] Therefore, the values of a culture have come to be almost synonymous with the conditions and psychological consequences of that culture, seen in detail as well as in general contours. But we must recognize that social action is not, in any culture, a duplication of its stated values. The link back to personal behavior of this cultural equipment is, nevertheless, very close indeed. Cassirer, in *An Essay on Man*, reports recent research on the psychopathology of language: "Patients suffering from aphasia or other kindred diseases have not only lost the use of words but have undergone corresponding changes in personality." Work by K. Goldstein and A. Gelb suggest that the loss or impairment of speech caused by brain injury is never "an isolated phenomenon," since such a defect alters the whole character of human behavior particularly where abstractions are required in cognitive thinking. Cassirer continues: "Without symbolism the life of man would be like that of the prisoners in the cave of Plato's famous simile. Man's life would be confined within the limits of his biological needs and his practical interests."[159] No person, not even the most constricted hebephrenic, lives wholly in Plato's cave. So with values. Perfection in them is rare from society to society and no one yet inhabits, with other millions, the perfect culture.

The chief linkages of values themselves are to symbols as culturally defined. Even here, there is a difference between ideal culture values and the reality situation. Disturbances which disorient a patient as to time, place, or the reality of actual circumstances about him may center, even in masked and disguised form, chiefly in disturbed relationships with other in one's immediate network of relationships and associations. Yet characteristic styles of interpersonal relationships in a society can color family functioning as readily as one's experience in a family can color his social relations. Few psychiatrists have escaped becoming at one time or another, father figures, or mother figures or sibling figures as the case might be. This kind of thought is peculiarly dependent upon cultural systems and symbols. If common symbols, such as these, become fraught with fear and uncertainty, or are colored and distorted with hostilities, they become problematic areas for the pursuit of rational thinking or even emotionalizing. But even dependency, hostility and fear can be injected into families. Affects appear disproportionately out of range where they are fostered with intensity in a whole culture. Over-and-under reactions become possible. A Thematic Apperception Test, or Rorschach evocation will produce father-male or mother-female symbolizations (in their relation to ego) as having unusual attributes in a culture where such attributes are nurtured. Yet no area of interest, economy, sex, religion, philosophy, or indeed, aging, authority, death, prestige, or illness, is, in any psychiatric or cultural theory, immune from such distortion.

Aberrant systems of thought and action or delusions which are always departures from "reality," are not made from whole cloth in an entirely private pattern. They refer to areas of stress, confusion, or outright aberration in the culture itself. Rather than culture *and* its symbols, being indistinguishable from psychosis, as in La Barre's theory, the symbols and value-orientations are so patterned and stylized as to provide the typical points of reference between the individual and "the reality he tests," if indeed he still can do so. While a cultural *insistence* upon a range of conduct is no burden on one whose symbol-usage is unimpaired, the entire matter of whether inadequate and self-destructive defenses are used, or whether sheer immaturity blocks growth, is dependent upon the nature of these cultural insistences in the first place.

Cultural values may be scrutinized for their universality or the chance they provide for alternatives. They may also be considered for their characteristic tendency to promote or thwart healthy development.

While it has been fashionable in psychoanalytic circles to attempt to define parental conduct or marital relation-

ships which "produce aberration" or reduce it, it is likely
that the social roles of mothers and of fathers in a given
setting, the nature of the marital institution, and the various social and economic qualifications upon human relationships in general constitute the real conditions of emotional existence. These conditions are visited upon individuals in all stages of the life cycle, become determinative
of individual role and are perpetuated or reduplicated by
tradition.

A recent study by Louise J. Despert among adolescent
and pre-adolescent children in the urban United States
has pointed to severe withdrawal, constriction and fear
among children suffering from obsessive-compulsive disorder, but greater fantasy, hostility, and weak, amorphous
ego-organization among schizophrenic children. The crucial factor for the psychotic children is that reality-testing
more generally fails and contact is more thoroughly lost.
In this light, the compulsions of the obsessive group appear
often as symbolic acts in *relation to reality*, and in terms of
which intellectual functioning and reality-testing are retained for the present. However tyrannically they are
used and distorted in symbolization, compulsions link to
reality. The relative *loss* of reality contact in the schizophrenias, though rarely complete, shows at the very least,
an inadequate reality-testing. In the schizo-affective disorders, the emotional imbalance and loss of realistic intellectual functioning go hand in hand as they do in the
schizophrenias generally. The point of referring to this
phrasing of the progression from psychoneurotic to psychotic states is to indicate that the partial loss of reality-
contact does not mean the irrelevancy to the patient of the
kind of reality experienced. Clinics and hospitals, since the
time of Adolf Meyer, or even before, are aware of the importance of the patient's current environmental setting.
In the same way, the kinds of communication a patient is

utilizing habitually and subtleties in the relationship of physician and adjunctive personnel to these patients least able to cope with negative features of their environment are significant features of modern therapy.[160]   There can be no doubt that even the most disturbed patients continue to read and interpret a socio-cultural environmental map.

Frieda Fromm-Reichman has written pointedly of the cultural factor as utilized by patients:[161]

"There are great differences of opinion, however, among various schools of psychoanalytic thinking in regard to the genetic frame of reference in which interpretation is done and about the patient's selection of content matter for repression and dissociation. The genetic frame of reference of psychoanalysts is oriented upon Freud's basic teachings of the fundamental significance of the developmental history in infancy and childhood. However, there is a difference in the interpretation of the events and emotional experience of the patient's early history, as determined by the psychosexual concepts of Freud *versus* the interpersonal interpretations of H. S. Sullivan. The patient's selection of subject matter for repression and dissociation, according to my thinking, is determined by the existing cultural standards governing his life. His medium of adherence to these standards is their acceptance by the significant people in his immediate environment and in his group."

We are indebted to Fromm-Reichman for putting the entire matter of patients' reaction-patterns in the framework of a functional and dynamic culture and personality scheme. Societies and cultures, no less than the normal and abnormal persons who constitute them, have their more or less patterned ways of doing things. Notions of proper behavior, styles of thought, and reactions to situations are governed by cultural standards designed to cope with the most usual problems of human conduct. While each individual handles these problems in his "own way," giving them his particular interpretation and personal stamp of approval, he neither creates the problems of his culture, nor in any but the most strained and unrealistic sense, singlehandedly accounts for their permanent solution. We are, especially in our Western culture so convinced of our uniqueness and variation from a nuclear pattern of behavior in common with others that we fail to see points of dependency upon those others who are constantly impinging upon, and often positively influencing, our development. This myth of absolute uniqueness is nowhere seen more clearly than in the schizophrenic with paranoid reaction who marks his departure from a pattern no longer acceptable by a personal denial of its reality. Here indeed there occurs a substitution of a highly individualized set of meanings. Few have seen in this, one type of reflection of a cultural standard. To one unaccustomed to the existence of patterns in culture and in behavior, these bizarre variations from a sense of identity with others are discussed as if only infantile regression were occurring. In the mildly narcissistic the same value system will often escape notice and go unobserved. What we often forget in these neurotic cases, as in the most bizarrely organized systems, is that there has been a highly influential social pattern to draw upon and even to vary, and that only experience within a cultural framework, no matter how unsatisfactory or painful in personal history, can cause this deviation.

Where personal experience within a cultural framework has taught one to vary or even to misconstrue its standards and values, we learn that patients can learn to fear them, hate them, or anxiously reject them. The cultural patterns of feeling, thought and action may include such mechanics as repression and guilt for sin and sex. But beyond that which is repressed as forbidden, or the degree to which shame or guilt are used in cultures, there are standards fragmentized and dissociated from other affective areas of thought and action. It is hackneyed to speak of nonacceptance or rejection by others, chiefly parental figures or their surrogates, as marking the first arousals of this sense of expected disapproval and consequent anxiety. How often, in our culture, is women's social and economic role stereotyped and condemned? The fact, even in mental hospitals, is that the arousals, unless skilfully avoided, can blend with other areas of resentment concerning male and female roles since they have long since become patterned behavior. The personality failures of individuals are often to a large extent failures in the social ethics and cultural system in which they operate.

This relationship between the individual and his sociocultural environment is the crux of the matter. The anthropologist, by studying the affectively-charged patterns of behavior of groups of people, both in terms of range and at their most typical or commonplace, can provide data on what Fromm-Reichman calls "the anxiety-provoking character of culturally unacceptable experiences." Not only do patients bar culturally unacceptable experiences from conscious awareness but they may be conditioned to do so either through dissociative or repressive mechanisms. One culture may promote fantasy projections in one area of living and another foster emotional abreactions of an activity sort in the same context. At the same time, if the inconsistencies and points of antagonism in the culture are studied, they may be seen to have direct effect on those rigidly adhering to its normative standards and becoming more directly involved in the cultural stress system. Among Western cultural traits producing unacceptable kinds of human experience and behavior, Fromm-Reichman has listed the growing extent and cruelty of war, the curbing of personal friendliness and its overt expression, the overdependency of adults, and the overpossessiveness or ideas of grandeur and magical thinking which Western cultures of our time actively promote.

The psychiatrist, who studies these patterns of reaction as developed in extreme forms within the total contours of a personality, still requires in his study of conspicuously deviant persons, a clearer statement of the standards or norms from which patients are recoiling. Here students of cultural values cannot take for granted that a coherent social environment, necessary for ego-integration, was available for the patient, or indeed, that unique traumatic events account for him alone. Before we can assess the degree of individual damage, it is necessary to plot not only a personal case history, but one in conjunction with the cultural standards and values to which the patient was exposed and to which he has reacted in some characteristic fashion. The individualization of a patient's treatment need not end when he is seen as being, in part, a product of his culture. Quite the contrary, in most cases it can only then begin.

The psychiatrist who makes cross-cultural corrections for standards and values guards against his own culturally-induced limitations, and adds to his insight and wisdom about human affairs. For some, according to Fromm-Reichman, such limitations interfere with the ability to see matters in a therapeutically valid perspective.[162] These attitudes about value concepts, even when they are not dogmatized, or given over to the extortion of "confessions" of a patient can be so closely adhered to that they amount to the therapist's insistence upon his own conventions or prejudices. Where the minimal task or first objective, quite often in therapy, is to develop in these patients the beginnings of self-esteem and the ability to live their own lives, standards and values must be provided to promote a sense of coherence and prevent chaotic disintegration. Even spontaneous self-expression has standards.

There are balances, in therapy, between over-relating and under-relating, between minimal expectations and the maximum elaboration of the most personalized choices and classifications of what is true or good. In some schools of psychoanalytic thinking, insight into a patient's *particular* history and *specific* cultural background is subordinated to a valuational scheme which insists on one course of development, or ontogenesis, from "polymorphous perversity" of the infant on out. A more positive and less fatalistic system was propounded by Otto Rank who noted that abnormality is by no means synonymous with maladjustment. In some societies, and even in some individual ethical systems, certain kinds of deviation from the norm are allowed and the abnormal individual is not necessarily maladjusted in his cultural setting. Such a typology of normal (adjusted), the ill or aberrant, and the creative artist, allows Rankians (and some interpreters of Erich Fromm) to describe as "normal" those who are said to have uncritically surrendered their individual wills and accepted the "will" of the group. The neurotic deviant is then described as one who cannot conform to the will of the group, and yet is not free to assert his own will, or individuality, in defiance of his group. Rank's third type, the artist, affirms his own will and is therefore free to assert or express truly constructive elements within himself whether these are contrary to standards or not. However, group standards in the systems of Rank or Fromm are defined in advance as being dull average.

Yet the anthropologist fears that those who are "tough" about cultural values are really the worst sentimentalists. Beyond the obvious yardstick of those things which are most beneficial to most people, or which the Benthamite would say produce health and happiness for the greatest number, the anthropologist does not see why all values must be declared at the start as existing in some hypotheti-

cal individual when they *emerge* in clearest form in actual
group living. Why must they be abstracted from one
person's behavior, when they are implicit and varying in
any enduring interpersonal relations? Why must they be
incorporated in absolute codes apart from science, when
all science is concerned, directly or indirectly, with human
values? Why must they be unchanging when human situations change? The fact that man is not the equal of his
body, that by virtue of his exploratory mental capacity, he
"condescends" to live in it, does not mean, as some philos-
ophers have put it, that the locus of behavior is wholly
biological and internal, or psychological, or cultural, or
merely individual at any one time. A Beethoven is never
so individualistic, or in a social sense, cultural as when he
presses an arbitrary cultural framework, the sonata form,
with its given aesthetic potentialities for balance or proportion, to the limits of emotional expression in a language
most people understand. Yet the necessity to speak the
language of emotions and individual interpretation of set,
given forms was so characteristic in Beethoven's day that
it stands in contrast to the unemotional experiments in
sound and orchestral color which come later. The subtle
and quiet understatement of Japanese painting of the
Kamakura period, as influenced by Zen Buddhist emphasis on "universal truths" which lie beyond the individual,
are a second example of values which are not centered in
the individual. Any reader of Elizabethan literature
knows that the English were once more emotionally demonstrative about personal affairs than they now are. Max
Mueller, in the Nineteenth Century, was told it was frivo-
lous for males to play the piano. We may be sure from
anthropological studies of music, literature and graphic or
plastic arts that there are norms over and beyond individual
variation which affect such variation. While there is no
such thing as an Italian race, there are variations, individ-

ual and regional, of an Italian language; and the same is true of Italian regional variants in character and expression.

In the study of mental disorder, we are not dealing with such positive emphases of the culture at all. The schizophrenic's elaborated fantasy life, denial of reality, and strange emotional and motility patterns lose something of this spirit of cultural epitomization, cultural enlargement, or even cultural adherence. Both the neurotic and the psychotic toning down of indentity and emotional communication with others, and their distortion or destruction of viable cultural symbols stand in opposition to the creative artist certainly, but they stand also in defiance of the average more positive interpretation of the values, standards and life patterns of the culture at its best. As stated earlier, aberration is not innovation and psychosis is not culture. But neither is creative innovation a wilful turning away from the interests and concerns of other people. Artists using one or another "language" or form of emotional communication, do of course express constructive elements within themselves, but they do so by expressing humanistic aspects of the culture within patterns which can reach others. If there are no satisfactory outlets for such constructive expression, an individual can repress or distort his sense of identity with others only at a wasteful cost of guilt and anxiety, or he can maintain the marginal "will" and adjustment of one who has lost in growth and development or is petrified by the thought of anything but the most rigid adherence.

Ernst Cassirer, in his *Essay on Man*, states that the difference between man and the infra-human Primates lies in the difference between a human, propositional language, based on symbols culturally defined, and an emotional language which animals possess as an affective system of signs and signals. Charles Morris and Leslie White, in

philosophy and anthropology respectively, have noted that
signals belong to the physical world of vertebrate being,
and symbols to the human world of meaning.   In this
sense, Charles Morris suggests that symbols are "desig-
nators" which in combination may themselves define what
is thought to be distinctive, desirable, proper behavior
influencing choice, or in short, matters *of value*, or of things
existent. The combination and blending in man of the two
languages, propositional and affective, has influenced some
scholars in denying what Cassirer calls "a creative or
constructive imagination" in animals beyond the practical, biological level. Such writers unhesitantly bestow on
man a "symbolic imagination and intelligence." However, these symbols, and hence the degrees of intelligence
and imagination they connote, derive from culture as an
adaptive or adjustive means in establishing controls in
the world of nature or the world of understanding (science,
myth, philosophy).   The world of interpersonal relations
is uniquely dependent on them.   That cultures are unconsciously patterned like languages and styles of art need
not surprize us; for even the component personalities of a
culture are dependent on *systems* of meanings understandable for other individuals, and likewise unconsciously patterned.   Sapir has suggested that this patterning of cultures, to be genuine, must be expressive of real human
needs and aspirations.   We may add that individuals, to
be healthy, must also express these crucial aspects of their
culture.

  The best in art, science and philosophy never fails in
human quality.   For these reasons, the complicated content of a values-system is always larger than the reach of
discrete individuals.   It is measured, in ultimate form,
again by human needs and aspirations, but translated now
into terms consistent with cultural situations and possibilities.   Thus, realistic values in a group and in a person can

function to narrow the distance between the real and ideal so far as these same needs and aspirations are concerned. In this sense, Cassirer is right that human cultures taken individually are systems of value, and taken as a whole the cultural process may well be the process of "man's progressive self-liberation." The process is not automatic however. The tensions and frictions in cultures and in mankind cannot be overlooked in philosophically viewing this panorama of achievement. It is dubious whether, in any real ethical sense of values, most people of the modern world enter fully into this domain of progress and self-liberation.

In their recent volume, *Social Science in Medicine*, Leo W. Simmons and Harold G. Wolff have commented on a wide range of sociocultural stresses which evoke "protective patterns" and promote or exacerbate illness and retard treatment. The social structure of a hospital and its functional organization, if related to such pre-existing patterns in the patient, may contain elements complicating or delaying recovery. Knowledge of sociocultural backgrounds along with the patient's adaptive or adjustive assets and liabilities which stem from long-established or recent methods of coping with stress are indispensable tools in reducing or eliminating "the very stressed-charged elements" that earlier provoked inept responses.[163] While it is likely that patients in general do not shed their sociocultural attributes with the onset of illness, it is equally true, as these authors point out, that little account is ordinarily taken in hospital centers of these pervasive and potent factors.

In psychiatry, however, the problem has been different. Here attention has long been paid to the problem of reaction formation and even to protective reaction patterns which are occasionally beneficial in the light of total personality assets and liabilities. Here again, the observation of personality patterns, in their total contours, is made with concern for character and temperament, individual assets and liabilities and the structure of psychopathology as it operates, or has operated, in the course of an entire life. Nor have family characteristics, or personality balances within them, been ignored. What we may say is that while there are known connections between family background and personality, persons responding ineptly to sociocultural stresses are viewed *on the symptom level of personalized disturbance without portraying inadequacies in the cultural value system.* A great deal of what is loosely charged to national "temperament" or personal "character" is really nothing, on scrutiny, but the effect of traditional patterns of conduct.

In a culture, for instance, that looks critically on informal demonstrativeness, the spontaneous human tendency known from children to display emotion spontaneously becomes more than normally inhibited. Since all human conduct is culturally modified, the task becomes one of looking more closely at those, like the Irish, which set greater store by fantasy, the "omnipotence of thought," the power of the word, and the oral expression of strivings and status aspirations. Such patterns may be more a matter of history, economy and family organization than a matter of nursing and weaning. Redlich, writing of normality and values, has written that: [164]

> "The normative approach is specific for a given culture. Although psychiatrists are just beginning to think in cultural anthropological terms . . . there is much less acceptance of the fact that most normative propositions are specific for a subculture . . . Kingsley Davis showed that our notions on mental hygiene are ideas of the middle class. There can be no doubt that culture to a large extent determines the scope of normality."

If again, the culture promotes the acting out of emotional

feeling directly, especially in given areas of life adjustment'
as in South Italy, can it be doubted that this will be felt
in the actual operations of the family of orientation (into
which one is born) and the family of procreation (in which
one later functions)?

The statistical approach, denoting both typical conduct
and the range of variation, is helpful at this point.   Edward Sapir, who studied perceptively the formal structure
and the particular quality or "genius" of a language, or of
language stocks and families, noted the general harmony or
consistency of these systems of expressive symbolism.   Yet
he concluded that the central tendencies of any language
system are imperfect in containing expressivity: "all gram-
mars leak."   It is possible, therefore, that a combined
cultural and clinical approach to the normal-abnormal
continuum will add to statistical knowledge on central
tendency and variation some further picture of the roots of
repression and dissociation among those who vary from
a norm.   We need special notice of the actual contexts in
which affect becomes disturbed or circumstantiality and
denial operate.   Before hostility can be combatted, we
must plot its course.   Or before the imbalances of identification and distortion of reality become "necessary," we
must know why they become necessary.   To accomplish
this, we need no new definitions of words like wish, hope,
attitudes, disparagement or dependency, nor novel definitions of mental health other than those already provided.
We must, however, have the temerity to question the
"perfection" and suitability of various styles of cultural
values, after searching them for operational imperfections,
for inconsistencies, for elements of confusion and aberration, and for inadequacies in promoting "man's progressive self-liberation."

A. Edel, a philosopher, has recently put the matter
similarly.   Writing of the search for unity in value phenom-

ena, he notes the prevalent tendency today to seek this unity in the exclusive terms of biological or psychological theory. Here he adds:[165]

> ". . . It is arbitrary postulation to assert that because man is an organism and all activity has a biological basis, therefore all aesthetic, political, religious, moral valuations *must* have biological *import* which only lack of knowledge prevents us from tracing . . . The hard-won lessons of the sciences of man concerning the relations of levels should not be surrendered in value theory."

Concerning Freudian psychology with its similar drive for exclusiveness, Edel states: " . . . It does not seem likely" that psychological unity will be achieved "without bringing social factors so far inside the structure as to make it no longer a purely psychological framework." Besides a possible cultural basis for a unitary value concept, "suggested by the anthropological concept of a culture pattern," Edel writes of an intercultural or cross-cultural, historical unity relating to the career of mankind in the world. He suggests with less exclusiveness and more interdisciplinary good sense that a final synthesis may come to represent "the growing unity of a knowledge of man."

To designate nearer goals or interpretations, and less distant consequences, we may say that in mental disorder the simplest human values, the possession of will power, decisiveness, the ability to control impulses while remaining spontaneous and socially considerate are denied many people of Western cultures. These are cultures with varying emphases on self-display and status, with the need for superiority and competitiveness in our own culture marking an extreme emphasis. The capacities for dispassionate detachment and self-analysis as any Buddhist well knows are no achievement of the Western world. Even insight into one's own emotional reactions and their bases suffer.

In Morita-therapy, in Japan, the latter emphases come naturally. It is not enough to chart these different cultural courses generally. The ability to live reasonably ordered lives, socially and culturally rewarding, with proper responsibilities and free from insecurities is statistically and qualitatively not characteristic of American sub-cultures. Allport's criteria of maturity, containing such character traits as objectivity, detachment, self-content, or even humor, or Leon Saul's of emotional development including high adaptability, low tendencies to regression, and minimal vulnerability, are not combined in most individuals. Obviously, the millenium is not here, but worse still it will not even be envisaged until the full force of behavioral and social sciences begin to challenge processes destructive of human happiness.

BIBLIOGRAPHY AND REFERENCES

1. HALLOWELL, A. I.: The self and its behavioral environment. *Explorations: Studies in Culture and Communication, 2;* 106-165, 1954.
2. OPLER, M. K.: Psychoanalytic techniques in social analysis. *J. of Social Psychol. 15;*91-127, 1942 (*Vide*, p. 115).
3. SULLIVAN, HARRY STACK: *The Interpersonal Theory of Psychiatry.* New York, Norton, 1953 (*Vide*, pp. xi, 365, 371, 376).
4. HALLOWELL, A. I.: *Popular Responses and Cultural Differences*, Rorschach Research Exchange, Vol. IX, 1945.
   HALLOWELL, A. I.: The Rorschach technique in the study of personality and culture, *Am. Anthropologist, 47:*No. 2, 1945.
5. THOMPSON, LAURA: *Culture in Crisis: A Study of the Hopi Indians:* or, Attitudes and acculturation. *Am. Anthropologist, 50:*No. 2, 1950.
6. HALLOWELL, A. I.: *Acculturation Processes and Personality Changes as Indicated by the Rorschach Technique.* Rorschach Research Exchange, Vol. VI, 1942.
7. DuBois, CORA,: *The People of Alor.* Minneapolis, Univ. Minnesota Press, 1944.
   GLADWIN, THOMAS, AND SARASON, S. B.: *Truk: Man in Paradise.* New York, Wenner-Gren Foundation Publications in Anthropology, No. 20, 1953.
8. HALLIDAY, J. L., *Psychosocial Medicine: A Study of the Sick Society.* New York, Norton, 1948.
9. KROEBER, A. L., AND KLUCKHOHN, C.: *Culture.* Papers of the Peabody Museum, Vol. 47, 1952 (*Vide*, p. 118).
10. CANNON, W. B.: *Bodily Changes in Pain, Hunger, Fear and Rage.* New York, Appleton, 1929.
    WOLFF, HAROLD G., Protective reaction patterns and disease. *Ann. Int. Med., 27:* 1947.
    GRACE, WILLIAM: Relationship of specific attitudes and emotions to certain bodily diseases. *Psychosom. Med. 14:No.* 4, 1952.
11. LIDDELL, HOWARD S.: Conditioning and emotions. *Scient. Am. 190:* No. 1, 1954. (Reference is also made to current work of Horsley Gantt.)
12. BLEULER, EUGEN: *Dementia Praecox or The Group of Schizophrenias.* New York, Internat. Univ. Press, 1950 (*Vide*, pp. 336, 463). See also: ZILBOORG, G. AND HENRY G. W.: *A History of Medical Psychiatry.* New York, Norton, 1941.
13. YAP, P. M.: The Latah reaction, *J. Men. Sc., 98;* 515-564, 1952.
14. HARE, E. H.: The ecology of mental disease, *J. Men. Sc. 98:*579-594, 1952.

15. FELIX, R. H., AND BOWERS, R. V.: Mental hygiene and socio-environmental factors. *Milbank Mem. Fund Quart. 26:*125-147, 1948.

16. BENEDICT, RUTH: Anthropology and the abnormal. *J. Genet. Psychol. 10:*59-82, 1934. Cf., HORNEY, KAREN: *New Ways in Psychoanalysis.* New York, Norton, 1939. Also, Redlich, F.: The concept of normality. *Am. J. Psychotherapy, 6:*551-576, 1952.

17. PARSONS, TALCOTT: *The Social System.* Glencoe, Illinois, Free Press, 1951.

18. FELIX, R. H., AND BOWERS, R. V.: *op.cit.,* p. 125.

19. DIETHELM, OSKAR: The Psychopathologic basis of psychotherapy of schizophrenia. Symposium, *Am. J. Psychiat., 111:*422-425, 1954.

20. DIETHELM, OSKAR: *Report of the Payne Whitney Psychiatric Clinic, New York Hospital,* 1953 (*Vide,* pp. 11-12).

21. GERARD, D. L., AND HUSTON, L.: Family setting and the social ecology of schizophrenia. *Psychiat. Quart., 27,* 1-12, 1953.
   GERARD, D. L., AND SIEGEL, JOSEPH; The family background of schizophrenia, *Psychiat. Quart., 24:*47-73, 1950.

22. HYDE, ROBERT, *et. al.* Studies in medical sociology. *New England J. Medicine, 231:*543-548, 571-577, 612-618, 1944.
   STOTT, L. S.: Environmental factors in relation to personality adjustments. *Rural Sociology, 10:* 1945.
   COUNTS, R. M., AND REGAN, PETER F.: Chronic schizophrenic reactions. *Monatsschr. f. Psychiatrie & Neurologie, 127:*47-60, 1954.

23. EATON, J. W., AND WEIL, R. J.: The mental health of the Hutterites. *Scient. Am. 189:* No. 1, 1953
   EATON, J. W., AND WEIL R. J.: The Hutterite mental health study. *Mennonite Quar. Rev.,* January, 1951.

24. HOLLINGSHEAD, A. B., AND REDLICH, F. C.: Social stratification and psychiatric disorders. *Am. Sociological Rev. 18:*No. 2, 1953.

25. DIETHELM, OSKAR: The alcohol problem. *Bull. New York Acad. Med. 29* (2nd Series): No.12, 1953.

26. FELIX, R. H., AND BOWERS, R. V.: *op.cit.*

27. RENNIE, T. A. C.: Prognosis in the psychoneuroses: benign and malignant developments, in HOCH, P. H., AND ZUBIN, J.: *Current Problems in Psychiatric Diagnosis.* New York, Grune & Stratton, 1953.

28. POWDERMAKER, HORTENSE: *Mass Communications Seminar.* New York, Wenner-Gren Foundation for Anthropological Research, 1953 (*Vide* especially, LASSWELL, HAROLD, Characteristics of media, pp. 82 ff.).

29. JONES, MAXWELL: *Social Psychiatry.* London, Tavistock Publications, 1952. See also: HEALY, WILLIAM, on the Borstal System.

30. RENNIE, T. A. C.: Psychiatry. *Ann. Rev. Med.,* pp. 253-260, 1953.

31. LING, THOMAS M.,: *Mental Health and Human Relations.* London, Lewis, 1954.

32. COTTRELL, LEONARD S., AND GALLAGHER, RUTH: *Developments in Social Psychology: 1930-1940.* New York, Beacon House, 1941.

33. LEMERT, E. M.: Exploratory study of mental disorders in a rural problem area. *Rural Sociology*, 13, 1948. See also: LEMERT, E. M.: *Social Pathology*. New York, McGraw-Hill, 1951.

34. COMPARE, LEMKAU, PAUL, TIETZE, CHRISTOPHER, AND COOPER, MARCIA: A survey of statistical studies on the prevalence and incidence of mental disorders in sample populations. *Pub. Health Rep. 58:* (December 31, 1943) (with methods and findings of the Roth-Luton Survey).

35. MANGUS, A.R.: *Mental Health of Rural Children in Ohio.* Ohio Agricultural Experiment Station, Research Bulletin, 682, 1949.

36. STOTT, L. S.: Environmental factors in relation to personality adjustments. *Rural Sociology, 10:* 1945.

37. EATON, J. W.: In defense of culture-personality studies. *Am. Sociological Rev. 16:*No. 1, 1951.

38. WOODARD, J. W.: The relation of personality structure to the structure of culture. *Am. Sociological Rev. 3:*No. 4, 1938.

39. BRILL, A. A.: *Lectures in Psychoanalytic Psychiatry*. New York, Knopf, 1949 (Lectures first given in 1924).

40. SELIGMAN, C. G.: Temperament, conflict and psychosis in a stone age population. *Brit. J. Med. Psychol. 9:*187-202, 1929.

41. DHUNJIBHOY, J.: Brief resume of the types of insanity commonly met with in India, *J. Ment. Sc., 16:*254-264, 1930.

42. STAINBROOK, E.: Some characteristics of the psychopathology of schizophrenic behavior in Bahian society. *Am. J. Psychiat. 109:*330-335, 1952.

43. VAN LOON, H. G., Protopathic instinctive phenomena in normal and pathologic Malay life. *Brit. J. M. Psychol. 8:*264-276, 1928.

44. DEVEREUX, G.: *Reality and Dream: Psychotherapy of a Plains Indian.* New York, Internat. Univ. Press, 1951.

45. SACHS, W.: *Black Hamlet.* Boston, Little, Brown, 1947.

46. MENNINGER, KARL: The contribution of psychoanalysis to American psychiatry. *Bull. Menninger Clin. 18:*85-96, 1954.

47. STAINBROOK, E.: *op.cit.*

48. STAINBROOK, E.: *op.cit.* Compare, for a general account of interior Brazil and coastal regions: LOPEZ, C., Ethnographische Betrachtungen über Schizophrenie. *Ztschr.: Ges. Neurol. u Psychiat., 142:*706-711, 1932.

49. CANNON, W. B.: Voodoo death. *Am. Anthropologist, 44:*No. 2, 1942.

50. GILLIN, JOHN: *The Culture of Security in San Carlos.* New Orleans, Middle American Research Institute, Series No. 16, 1951 (*Vide* pp. 112 ff.). See also:
    GILLIN, JOHN: Magical fright. *Psychiatry, 11:*387-400, 1948.

51. HENRY, JULES: Anthropology and psychosomatics. *Psychom. Med. 11:* 216-222, 1949.

52. EBAUGH, FRANKLIN G., Psychosomatic medicine, *International Forum*, Vol. 2, No. 3, 1954.

53. WINSTON, E.: The alleged lack of mental disease among primitive groups. *Am. Anthropologist. 36*, No. 2, 1934.
MEAD, MARGARET: *Coming of Age in Samoa.* New York, William Morrow, 1928.

54. JOSEPH, ALICE, AND MURRAY, V. F.: *Camorros and Carolinians of Saipan: Personality Studies.* Cambridge, Harvard, 1951.

55. RÓHEIM, GEZA: Racial differences in the neuroses and psychoses. *Psychiatry, 2-3;* 375-390, 1939.
YAP, P. M.: Mental diseases peculiar to certain cultures: a survey of comparative psychiatry. *J. Ment. Sc. 97:*313-327, 1951.

56. CARPENTER, E. S.: Witch fear among the Aivilik Eskimos. *Am. J. Psychiatry, 110:*No. 3, 1953.

57. BERNDT, R. M., AND BERNDT, C.: The concept of abnormality in an Australian aboriginal society, in: WILBUR, G. B. AND MUENSTERBERGER, W.: *Psychoanalysis and Culture.* New York, Internat. Univ. Press, 1951.

58. JACOBSON, A., AND BERENBERG, A. N.: Japanese psychiatry and psychotherapy. *Am. J. Psychiatry, 109:*No. 5, 1952.

59. MITTELMAN, B., WOLFF, HAROLD G. AND SHARF, MARGARET: *Emotions and gastroduodenal functions. Psychoso. Med. 4:*51-61, 1942.

60. STOUFFER, SAMUEL, *et. al.*: *The American Soldier:* Vol. IV, *Measurement and Prediction.* Princeton, Princeton Univ. Press, 1950.

61. ACKERKNECHT, E. H.: Psychopathology, Primitive medicine and primitive culture. *Bull. Hist. Med. 14:*30-67, 1943.

62. PARSONS, TALCOTT: Some comments on the general theory of action. *Am. Sociological Rev. 18:*618-631, 1953.

63. FELIX, R. H. AND BOWERS, R. V.: *op.cit.*, pp. 131 ff.

64. HENRY, JULES: Family Structure and the transmission of neurotic behavior. *Am. J. Orthopsychiat. 21,*800-818, 1951.

65. GORDON, J. E., O'ROURKE, E., RICHARDSON, F. L. W., AND LINDEMANN, ERICH: Preventive medicine and epidemiology. *Am. J. Med. Sc. 223:* 316-343, 1952.

66. GRUENBERG, E. M.: Community conditions and psychoses of the elderly. *Am. J. Psychiatry, 110:*No. 12, 1954. (The psychoses dealt with are cerebral arteriosclerosis and senile psychosis.)

67. HOLLINGSHEAD, A. B., AND REDLICH, F. C.: Social stratification and psychiatric disorders. *Am. Sociological Rev. 18:* No. 2, 1953.

68. FARIS, R. E. L., AND DUNHAM, H. W.: *Mental Disorders in Urban Areas: An Ecological Study of Schizophrenia and Other Psychoses.* Chicago Univ. Chicago Press, 1939, p. 53.

69. SCHWARTZ, MORRIS S.: The economic and spatial mobility of paranoid schizophrenics and manic depressives. Master's Thesis, University of Chicago, 1946 (unpublished).

70. ROBINSON, W. S.: Ecological correlations and the behavior of individuals. *Am. Sociological Rev. 15:*351-357, 1950.

71. JONES, MAXWELL, *op.cit.*

72. LEWIS, AUBREY: Social aspects of psychiatry. *Edinburgh M. J.*, *58:* 214, 1951.

73. SPITZ, RENE A.: *The Psychogenic Diseases in Infancy: The Psychoanalytic Study of the Child.* New York, Internat. Univ. Press, 1951.

74. BOWLBY, JOHN: *Maternal Care and Mental Health.* Geneva, World Health Organization, Monograph Series No. 2, 1951.

75. BALES, R. F.: Cultural differences in rates of alcoholism. *Quar. J. Stud. Alcohol.* *6:*480-493, 1946.

76. HYDE, ROBERT, *et. al.*: *op. cit. New England J. Medicine*, *231:*Part III, Table III, 1944.

77. STRAUSS, J. H. AND STRAUSS, M. A.: Suicide, homicide, and social structure in Ceylon. *Am. J. Sociology*, *58:*No. 5, 1953 (*Vide*, Table I, p. 462, and commentary).

78. CHESS, STELLA, CLARK, KENNETH B., AND THOMAS, ALEXANDER: The importance of cultural evaluation in psychiatric diagnosis and treatment. *Psychiatric Quart.* 27:102-114, 1953

79. LEWIS, AUBREY: Points of research into the interaction between the individual and the culture, in: TANNER, J. M.: *Prospects in Psychiatric Research.* Oxford, The Proceedings of the Oxford Conference of the Mental Health Research Fund, 1953.

80. LEMERT, E. M., *Social Pathology, op. cit.*

81. STANTON, A. H., AND SCHWARTZ, M. S.: Observations on dissociation as social participation. *Psychiatry*, *12:*339-354, 1949.

82. REDLICH, F. C. AND BINGHAM, JUNE: *The Inside Story: Psychiatry and Everyday Life.* New York, KNOPF, 1953, pp. 192-3.

83. DIETHELM, OSKAR,: *Annual Report of the Payne Whitney Psychiatric Clinic*, 1953, *op. cit.*, pp. 9-12.

84. SAPIR, EDWARD: The unconscious patterning of behavior in society, in: DUMMER, E. S., *The Unconscious.* New York, Knopf, 1929, pp. 114-142. .

85. KLUCKHOHN, FLORENCE R.: Dominant and substitute profiles of cultural orientation. *Social Forces*, *28:*No. 4, 1950.

86. DUNHAM, H. W.: The social personality of the catatonic-schizophrene. *Am. J. Sociology*, *49:*508-518, 1944.

87. CLAUSEN, JOHN A., AND KOHN, M. L., The use of the ecological method in social psychiatry. (Mss. from the Laboratory of Socio-Environmental Studies.) Bethesda, Maryland, National Institute of Mental Health, U. S. Public Health Service, 1954.

88. SCHAFFER, LESLIE, AND MYERS, J. K.: Psychotherapy and social stratification. *Psychiatry*, *17:*83-93, 1954.

89. ALEXANDER, FRANZ, AND SZASZ, THOMAS S.: The psychosomatic approach in medicine, in: ALEXANDER, FRANZ, AND ROSS, HELEN, *Dynamic Psychiatry.* Chicago, Univ. Chicago Press, 1952 (pp. 369-400).

90. ALEXANDER, FRANZ: *Psychosomatic Medicine.* New York, Norton, 1950.

91. RUESCH, JURGEN, *et. al.*,: *Chronic Disease and Psychological Invalidism.* Berkeley, Univ. California Press, 1946.

92. CAUDILL, WILLIAM, REDLICH, F. C., GILMORE, H. R., AND BRODY, W.: Social structure and interaction processes on a psychiatric ward. *Am. J. Orthopsychiat. 22:*314-334, 1952.

93. DEVEREUX, GEORGE: Psychiatry and anthropology. *Bull. Menninger Clinic. 16:*167-177, 1952.

94. MACKAY, D.: A background for African psychiatry. *East African M. J., 25:*1-10, 1948.

95. CAROTHERS, J. C.: *The African Mind in Health and Disease.* Geneva, World Health Organization, Monograph Series No. 17, 1953. (This study is a careful collation of data from almost two hundred references and direct studies to African psychiatry from various parts of the continent. For accurate summarization and intelligent sifting of data, it is recommended; for inept statements of "the African mind" in general, as reflected in the title, it is not recommended.)

96. LAUBSCHER, B. : *Sex, Custom, and Psychopathology.* London, Routledge, 1937.

97. CAROTHERS, J. C.: A study of mental derangement in Africans and an attempt to explain its peculiarities, more especially in relation to the African attitude to life. *Psychiatry, 11:*47-85, 1948. (Here the above comment on Carothers' recent work applies with greater force. His other work on "frontal lobe functioning" in the African, questionable from the point of view of physical anthropology, may be found in: CAROTHERS, J. C.: Frontal lobe function and the African. *J. Med. Sc. 97:*12-47, 1951; Also, *J. Ment. Sc. 93:*548,1948).

98. TOOTH, G.: *Studies in Mental Illness in the Gold Coast* (Colonial Research Publications No. 6) London, His Majesty's Stat. Offi. 1950.

99. BROCK, J. F., AND AUTRET, M.: *Kwashiorkor in Africa.* Geneva, World Health Organization, Monograph Series No. 8, 1952.

100. CAROTHERS, J. C.: *op. cit.*, 1953, p. 140. (Cf., Carothers, J. C.: *J. Ment. Sc. 97:*12, 1951.)

101. CAROTHERS, J. C.: *op.cit.*, 1953, p. 159.

102. MALZBERG, BENJAMIN A., *Social and Biological Aspects of Mental Disease.* Utica, New York, State Hospitals Press, 1940. (Comprises journal articles published elsewhere.) See also: MALZBERG, BENJAMIN A., Rates of mental disease among certain population groups in New York State. *J. Am. Statistical Asso. 31:*1936; and article by MALZBERG, in KLINEBERG, OTTO: *Characteristics of the American Negro.* New York, publ. Negro in American Life Series, 1944.

103. CAROTHERS, J. C.: *op.cit.*, 1953, p. 163.

104. AUBIN, H.: *L'homme et la Magie.* Paris, 1952.

105. CAROTHERS, J. C.: *op cit.*, 1953, p. 142.

106. CAROTHERS, J. C.: *op. cit.*, 1953, p. 148.

107. CAROTHERS, J. C.: *op. cit.*, 1953, p. 161.

108. BEAGLEHOLE, ERNEST: Culture and psychosis in New Zealand, *J. Polynesian Society*, 48:144, 1939.

109. BEAGLEHOLE, ERNEST: *Some Modern Hawaiians: Culture and Psychosis in Hawaii.* Honolulu, T. H., Univ. Hawaii Research Publications, No. 19, 1939.

110. HALLOWELL, A. I.: *Acculturation Processes and Personality Change as Indicated by Rorschach Technique.* Rorschach Research Exchange, Vol. VI, 1942, pp. 42-50.
    HALLOWELL, A. I.: Culture and mental disorder, *J. Abnor. & Social Psychol.* 29:1-9, 1934.

111. LANDES, RUTH: The abnormal among the Ojibwa Indians. *J. Abnor. & Social Psychol.* 33:14-33, 1938.

112. COOPER, J. M.: Mental disease situations in certain cultures. *J. Abnor. & Social Psychol.* 29:10-17, 1934.

113. HALLOWELL, A. I.: Cultural factors in the structuralization of perception, in ROHRER, J. H. AND SHERIF, M.: *Social Psychology at the Crossroads.* New York, Harper, 1951.

114. HALLOWELL, A. I.: Some psychological aspects of measurement among the Salteaux. *Am. Anthropologist.* 44:No. 1, 1942.

115. JOSEPH, ALICE, AND MURRAY, V. F.: *Chamorros and Carolinians of Saipan: Personality Studies.* Cambridge, Harvard, 1951, p. 199.

116. ABERLE, D. F.: 'Arctic Hysteria' and Latah in Mongolia. *Tr. New York Acad. Sc.* 14:291-297, 1952.

117. ACKERKNECHT, E. H.: Psychopathology, primitive medicine, and primitive culture. *op. cit.*, 1943.

118. VAN LOON, H. G.: *op. cit.*, 1928.

119. DEVEREUX, G.: A sociological theory of schizophrenia. *Psychoanalyt. Rev.* 26:315-342, 1934.

120. DEWEY, JOHN: *Human Nature and Conduct.* New York, Henry Holt, 1922, (part II, section 5, p. 131).

121. BAILEY, FLORA L.: Navajo motor habits, *Am. Anthropologist,* 44: No. 2, 1942.

122. ASTROV, MARGOT: The concept of motion as the psychological leitmotif of Navajo life and literature. *J. Am. Folklore,* 63:45-56, 1950.

123. BELO, JANE: The Balinese temper. *Character and Personality,* 4, 120-146, 1935.

124. DEVEREUX, G.: Mohave Indian verbal and motor profanity, in ROHEIM, GÉZA, *Psychoanalysis and the Social Sciences.* New York, Internat. Univ. Press, 1951.

125. BARNOUW, VICTOR: The fantasy world of a Chippewa woman. *Psychiatry* 12:67-76, 1949.

126. HALLOWELL, A. I.: Shabwan: a dissocial Indian girl. *Am. J. Orthopsychiat.* 8:329-340, 1938.
    SPENCER, KATHERINE: Mythology and values: an analysis of Navajo

Chantway myths. Doctoral thesis, submitted for publication in Papers of the Peabody Museum, Harvard, 1952.

127. LINCOLN, J. S.: *The Dream in Primitive Cultures.* Baltimore, Williams & Wilkins, 1935.

128. SPENCER, D. M.: Fijian dreams and visions, in DAVIDSON, D. S.: *Twenty-Fifth Anniversary Studies.* Publications of the Philadelphia Anthropological Society, 1, 199-209, 1937.

129. EGGAN, DOROTHY: The manifest content of dreams. *Am. Anthropologist, 54:*No. 4, 1952.

130. EFRON, DAVID: *Gesture and Environment.* New York, King's Crown Press (Columbia University), 1941.

131. LOWIE, R. H.: *Social Organization.* New York, Rinehart, 1948. (For the points made, *vide,* pp. 15, 281, 318, ff., 322, 387).

132. LEMKAU, PAUL, AND DeSANCTIS, CARLO: A survey of Italian psychiatry. *Am. J. Psychiat. 107:* 401-408, 1950.

133. BERNE, ERIC: Some Oriental mental hospitals. *Am. J. Psychiat. 106:* 376-383, 1950.

134. WHITEHEAD, ALFRED NORTH: *Introduction to Mathematics.* New York, Henry Holt, 1911, p. 223.

135. OPLER, M. K.: *op. cit.,* 1942.

136. FROMM, ERICH: Sex and character, in GEDDES, DONALD P., AND CURIE, ENID; *About the Kinsey Report.* New York, New American Library, 1948, pp. 56-7.

137. LEMKAU, PAUL, PASAMANIK, BENJAMIN, AND COOPER, MARCIA: The implications of the psychogenetic hypothesis for mental hygiene. *Am. J. Psychiat. 110:*436-442, 1953.

138. HENRY, G. W., *Sex Variants: A Study of Homosexual Patterns.* New York, Hoeber, 1941 (2 Vols., pp. 1179; *vide,* summaries of male cases: pp. 3-14; and of female cases, pp. 549-556).

139. ROBB, J. H.: Clinical studies of marriage and the family: a symposium, on methods. *Brit. J. M. Psychol. 26,* 215-221, and parts 3, 4, 1953.
    NAEGELE, KASPAR D.,: Hostility and aggression in middle-class American families. Doctoral thesis (Unpublished), Harvard, 1951.

140. SULLIVAN, HARRY STACK: *The Psychiatric Interview.* (Edited by Helen S. Perry and Mary L. Gawel.) New York, Norton, 1954, pp. 28-32, 37-38.

141. ROBERTS, BERTRAM H., AND MYERS, J. K.: Religion, national origin, immigration, and mental disorders. *Am. J. Psychiat. 110:*759-764, 1954.

142. OPLER, M. K.: Cu'tural perspectives in mental health research. *Am. J. Orthopsychiat. 25:*51-59, 1955.

143. FREUD, S.: *Die Traumdeutung,* 3rd Ed. Leipzig and Vienna, Transl. by A. A. Brill, *Interpretation of Dreams.* London, George Allen, 1911.

144. OPLER, M. K.: *op cit.,* 1942 (*Vide,* pp. 118-127). See also:
    OPLER, M. K.: The Southern Ute of Colorado, in Linton, Ralph (Ed.)

Acculturation in Seven American Indian Tribes. New York, Appleton, 1940.

145. STUNKARD, ALBERT: Some interpersonal aspects of an oriental religion. *Psychiatry, 14-4:*419-431, 1951.

146. OPLER, M. K. (with SPICER, E. H., AND LUOMALA, K): *Impounded People.* Washington, U.S. Department of Interior, 1946.

147. OPLER, M. K.: Anthropology, in HARRIMAN, P. L. (Ed.): *Contemporary Social Science.* Harrisburg, Pennsylvania, Stackpole, 1953. (*Vide,* section, Culture-Personality Theory: A Methodological Review of a Current in American Anthropology, pp. 328-344).

148. SAPIR, EDWARD: The contribution of psychiatry to an understanding of behavior in society. *Am. J. Sociology. 42:*862-870, 1937.

149. KLUCKHOHN, CLYDE: The influence of psychiatry on anthropology in America during the past one hundred years, in HALL, J. K., ZILBOORG, G., AND BUNKER, H. A.: *One Hundred Years of American Psychiatry.* New York, Columbia Univ. Press, 1944.

150. KLEIN, G. S., HOLTZMAN, P. S., AND LASKIN, D.: The perception project: progress report for 1953-54. *Bull. Menninger Clinic, 18:*260-266, 1954.

151. HARTMANN, HEINZ: Ego psychology and the problem of adaptation, in RAPAPORT, DAVID: *Organization and Pathology of Thought.* New York, Columbia Univ. Press, 1951.

152. KRIS, ERNST: On preconscious mental processes, in RAPAPORT, DAVID: *op. cit.*

153. RAPAPORT, DAVID: The autonomy of the ego. *Bull. Menninger Clin.* 15:113-123, 1951.

154. HSU, FRANCIS L. K.: Suppression versus repression. *Psychiatry, 12-3:* 223-242, 1949.

155. WEGROCKI, H. J.: A critique of cultural and statistical concepts of abnormality, in KLUCKHOHN, CLYDE, AND MURRAY, H. A.: *Personality in Nature, Society, and Culture.* New York, KNOPF, 1948.

156. LABARRE, WESTON: *The Human Animal.* Chicago, Univ. Chicago Press, 1954.

157. FEIBLEMAN, JAMES K.: Towards an analysis of the basic value system. *Am. Anthropologist 56:*421-432, 1954.

158. KLUCKHOHN, CLYDE: Values and value orientations, in PARSONS, TALCOTT, AND SHILS, E. A.: *Toward a General Theory of Action.* Cambridge, Harvard, 1951 (*Vide,* p. 411).

159. CASSIRER, ERNST: *An Essay on Man.* Garden City, New York, Doubleday, 1953 (*Vide,* p. 62).

160. STANTON, A. H., AND SCHWARTZ, M. S.: *The Mental Hospital.* New York, Basic Books, Inc., 1954.

161. FROMM-REICHMAN, FRIEDA: *Principles of Intensive Psychotherapy.* Chicago, Univ. Chicago Press, 1950 (*Vide,* pp. 82-84).

162. FROMM- REICHMAN, FRIEDA: *op. cit.,* pp. 32-33.

163. SIMMONS, LEO, AND WOLFF, HAROLD G.: *Social Science in Medicine*. New York, Russell Sage Foundation, 1954 (*Vide*, pp. 196-197).

164. REDLICH, F. C.: The concept of normality. *Am. J. Psychotherapy*, *6-3:* 551-576, 1952 (*Vide*, p. 558).

165. EDEL, ABRAHAM: The concept of values in contemporary philosophical value theory. *Philosophy of Science, 20-3:*198-207, 1954 (*Vide*, pp. 202-204).

INDEX

A

Aberle, David F., 225
Abraham, Karl, 26, 188
Acculturation, 6, 17, 23, 35-37, 65, 71, 75, *See also:* Culture change
in disease incidence, 91
effects on incidence rates in New Zealand, 128
effect on mental illness in Africa, 120
in Hawaii, 129, 130, 134
rates of change, 99
among Salteaux Indian groups, 130
and schizophrenia, 80
and symptomatology, 74
variations in personality formation, 57
Ackerknecht, Erwin H., 86, 133, 222, 225
Adler, Alfred, 147
Admission rates, Italian hospitals 141, *See also* Incidence rates, Epidemiological studies and surveys
Affective disorders in foreign born, 163
Africa, 74, 142, 153, 158, 160
Ba Thonga, 23, 57, 154
Bemba of North Rhodesia, 123
East, 168
Forest Bantu, 80
Kenya, 17
Masai, 176
South African, 120; West African, 115
incidence rates, discussion of psy-

chiatric studies and surveys, pp. 114 ff
Alcoholism, 26, 46, 47, 69
Irish, 163
Alexander, Franz, 111, 223
Algren, Nelson, 95
Allport, Gordon, 218
American ethnic groups, 65, *See also* Czech, German, etc.
American mental institutions, 70, *See also* Mental institutions in other countries
Amok, 71, 124, 198
Amok described, Asian, African, Fuegian, 133, 134
Amok in West Africa, 125
Andaman Islanders, 186
Anomie, 34, 35, 64
definition of, 34
Anthropologists, cultural, 13, 58, 153
data, 208
physical, 12
Anthropology, 5-9, 16
Anthropology, cultural, xi, 10, 31, 56
and relationship to psychiatry, 59, 60
Anthropology
culture-personality studies, 89
ethics and values studies, 59
family studies, 155
literature, 169
materials, 20, 24, 58
methods of study, 51
monographs, 21
psychiatrist and psychological studies, 54, 58, 71, 148, 162
use of literature to psychiatry, 169

229

This Book

CULTURE, PSYCHIATRY AND HUMAN VALUES

By

MARVIN K. OPLER, PH.D.

was set, and printed by the Rogers Printing Company of Dixon, Illinois. The page trim size is 5½ x 8½ inches. The type page is 23 x 39 picas. The type face is Baskerville, set 11 point on 13 point. The text paper is 70-lb Ibsen eggshell. The binding was by Pantagraph Printing & Stationery Company of Bloomington, Illinois. The cover is Roxite SL Vellum, 5175, 11-M, Two-tone black.

With THOMAS BOOKS *careful attention is given to all details of manufacturing and design. It is the Publisher's desire to present books that are satisfactory as to their physical qualities and artistic possibilities and appropriate for their particular use.* THOMAS BOOKS *will be true to those laws of quality that assure a good name and good will.*